Cooperative Learning

Grammar

Melissa Agnew
Stefanie McKoy

Kagan

Kagan Publishing
981 Calle Amanecer
San Clemente, CA 92673
1 (800) 933-2667
www.KaganOnline.com

ISBN: 978-1-933445-30-4

Cooperative Learning & Grammar
TABLE OF CONTENTS

TABLE OF CONTENTS

Grammar Skills 2
PARTS OF SPEECH (continued)

Grammar Skills 3
PUNCTUATION

Grammar Skills 4
SENTENCES

TABLE OF CONTENTS

Grammar Skills 4
SENTENCES (continued)

Grammar Skills 5
WORKING WITH WORDS

ANSWER KEY

ABOUT THE AUTHORS

Melissa Agnew graduated from Missouri State University in Springfield, Missouri, with a Bachelor of Arts degree in Elementary Education and a Master of Arts degree in Educational Administration. She has taught third grade for seven years in the Branson School District. In those seven years, she received her eMINTS certification and served as both team leader and curriculum leader. Additionally, Melissa has worked with groups of English Language Learners and Gifted Student Clusters in her regular education classroom. She resides in Springfield, Missouri, with her husband and their young son. She enjoys cooking, going to the gym, and taking care of her family.

Stefanie McKoy graduated from Missouri State University in Springfield, Missouri, with a Bachelor of Arts degree in Elementary Education and earned a Master of Arts degree in Educational Technology Leadership from the University of Arkansas in Fayetteville. She is currently certified in both Early Childhood and Elementary Education, and has her eMINTS certification. Stefanie teaches third grade at Branson School District. She has served on her school's communication arts committee and was coordinator for the after-school tutoring program serving four grade levels and over 100 students. She has been teaching with the special education department serving eight learning disabled students in her regular education classroom. Stefanie resides in Ozark, Missouri, with her husband and their young son. She enjoys reading, running outdoors, and drinking coffee.

Welding (verb)
Boy (Noun) Subject (Simple)
Girl (Antonym)
is (helping verb)

THE BOY IS WELDING.
(telling sentence)

THANK YOU

Thanks go to Laurie Kagan and Miguel Kagan, for the feedback and for the opportunity to share this book with others; Heather Malk and Jeremie Rujanawech for making the book come alive with the design; Becky Herrington for managing the publication; Alex Core for cover design and color; Erin Kant for illustrations, and Ginny Harvey for copyediting.

We would like to thank James Larimore from Branson Photography for taking our pictures for the book.

—M.A. and —S.M.

Cooperative Learning & Grammar
Kagan Publishing • 1 (800) 933-2667 • www.KaganOnline.com

INTRODUCTION

Dear Educator,

Thank you for taking interest in *Cooperative Learning & Grammar*. We have worked very hard to bring you the best activities to use in the classroom. As current educators ourselves, we saw a need to have more activities on hand. If you are like us, you'll find using Kagan Cooperative Structures will greatly improve classroom learning. We were continually creating worksheets and activities to use in the classroom, and since we found ourselves using our activities numerous times and other teachers were coming to us for our creations, we decided to compile it all into a book to share with you!

The structures you will most commonly find in this book include Find Someone Who, RallyCoach or Sage-N-Scribe, and Find-N-Fix. We know that teachers are still often held to collecting grades and showing student learning through "worksheet" activities. We tried to provide you with several activities for each content standard utilizing different structures. We also tried to provide scaffolding activities to increase understanding during lessons. We included a few Quiz-Quiz-Trade, Fan-N-Pick or Showdown, and Mix-N-Match activities as we know these are some of our students' favorites.

During the process of creating this book, we had overwhelming encouragement and assistance from our friends at Branson Elementary West in Branson, Missouri. We could not have done it without all the uplifting e-mails and willingness to try out our activities in the classroom. We also thank our principal, Mike Dawson, for being understanding of our continued endeavors and always providing any support we might need. We must also thank our students who were our mini-editors and testers! They were never afraid to share their opinions. We would also like to thank Michelle Brown for reviewing and offering suggestions from a literacy coach's perspective.

In addition, we would like to extend a huge thank-you to our families for the continuous support and understanding as we worked on our activities. We couldn't have done it without you!

So, we leave you with our collection of grammar activities for grades K-2. Enjoy the fun your students will have while learning in your classroom!

Melissa Agnew
Stefanie McKoy

Your partners in education,
Melissa Agnew and Stefanie McKoy

STRUCTURES

RALLYCOACH

Partners take turns, one solving a problem while the other coaches.

Setup: The teacher prepares a set of problems. Each pair receives the problem worksheet or a piece of paper to answer the problems and one pencil or pen.

1 **Partner A Solves**
In shoulder partners, Partner A solves the first problem, talking about his or her thinking.

2 **Partner B Coaches**
Partner B acts as the coach. Partner B watches, listens, and checks. If Partner A gets an incorrect answer or needs help, Partner B coaches. If Partner A solves the problem correctly, Partner B praises.

3 **Partner B Solves**
Students switch roles and Partner B now solves the problem, talking about it.

4 **Partner A Coaches**
Partner A now acts as the coach: watching, listening, checking, coaching, and praising.

5 **Continue Solving**
The process is repeated for each new problem.

Variations

• **RallyCoach for Oral Problems.** The teacher gives the class problems orally, and students use RallyCoach to solve the problems.

RallyCoach ACTIVITIES

SAGE-N-SCRIBE

Partners take turns being the Sage and Scribe.

Setup: In pairs, Student A is the Sage; Student B is the Scribe. Each pair is given a set of problems to solve, half for each partner. Partners can share a pencil or pen.

1 Sage Instructs Scribe
The Sage orally instructs the Scribe how to perform a task or solve a problem. For example, the Sage's instructions to the Scribe for correcting sentences with capitalization might sound like this: *"To fix this sentence, write the sentence with correct capitalization."*

2 Scribe Writes Solution, Tutors if Necessary
The Scribe solves the problem in writing according to the Sage's step-by-step oral instructions. If the Sage gives incorrect instructions, the Scribe tutors the Sage. *"I don't think that's correct. I think...".*

3 Scribe Praises Sage
After completion of the problem, the Scribe praises the Sage. *"You aced that one!"*

4 Partners Switch Roles
Students switch roles for the next problem or task.

Hints

• **Polite Tutoring.** Sometimes the Sage will make errors in his or her instructions. Teach the class how to politely tell their partners that they missed a step or made an error. Reinforce that the point is not to see who is smarter or to see who can make the fewest errors. The goal is for everyone to work together and for everyone to learn.

• **Checkpoint.** Have a place in the room where students can go to check answers if both partners are stuck.

Grammar Skills 1
SYNONYMS & ANTONYMS

Grammar Skills 2
PARTS OF SPEECH

Grammar Skills 3
PUNCTUATION

Grammar Skills 4
SENTENCES

Grammar Skills 5
WORKING WITH WORDS

Quiz-Quiz-Trade

Students quiz a partner, get quizzed by a partner, and then trade cards to repeat the process with a new partner.

Setup: The teacher provides or students create cards, each with a grammar problem.

1 **Students Pair Up**
With a card in one hand and the other hand raised, each student stands up, puts a hand up, and pairs up with a classmate. They give each other a high five as they pair up. *"Alright everyone, stand up, hand up, pair up. High five when you pair up and lower your hands so everyone can quickly find a partner with a hand up."*

2 **Partner A Quizzes**
In the pair, Partner A asks Partner B a question relating to his or her card. For example, *"My card says* didn't. Didn't *is a contraction for what two words?"*

3 **Partner B Answers**
Partner B answers Partner A's question: *"did not."*

4 **Partner A Praises or Coaches**
If Partner B answers correctly, Partner A praises him or her. If Partner B answers incorrectly, Partner A provides the correct answer and coaches or tutors Partner B.

5 **Partners Switch Roles**
Partners switch roles. Partner B now asks the question and offers praise or coaches.

6 **Partners Trade Cards**
Before departing and looking for new partners, partners trade cards. This way, students have a new card for each new pairing.

7 **Continue Quizzing and Trading**
Partners split up and continue quizzing and getting quizzed by new partners. When done, they trade cards again and find a new partner.

Quiz-Quiz-Trade
ACTIVITIES

Find Someone Who

Students circulate through the classroom, forming and reforming pairs, trying to "find someone who" knows an answer, then they become "someone who knows."

Setup: The teacher prepares a worksheet or questions for students.

1 Students Mix
With worksheets in one hand and the other hand raised, students circulate through the room until they find a partner. *"Mix in the room and pair up with a student with a hand up. Put your hands down and ask each other one question from your sheet. If your partner knows an answer, write the answer in your own words, then have your partner sign your sheet to show your partner agrees."*

2 Partner A Asks a Question
In pairs, Partner A asks a question from the worksheet; Partner B responds. Partner A records the answer on his or her own worksheet.

3 Partner B Checks
Partner B checks the answer and initials it that he or she agrees.

4 Partner B Asks a Question
Partner B now asks a question; Partner A responds. Partner B records the answer on his or her own worksheet.

5 Partner A Checks
Partner A checks the answer and initials it that he or she agrees.

6 Partners Depart
Partners shake hands, part, and raise a hand again as they search for a new partner.

7 Continue Finding Someone Who
Students continue mixing and pairing until their worksheets are complete.

8 Students Sit
When their worksheets are completed, students sit down; seated students may be approached by others as a resource.

9 Teams Compare Answers
When all students are done, or the teacher calls time, students return to their teams to compare answers; if any disagreement or uncertainty arises, they can consult a neighbor team or raise four hands to ask a team question. *"Please return to your team and RoundRobin read the question and share the answer. If you have different answers, work it out in your team. If you can't agree, get help from a nearby team, or ask a team question."*

Variations

• **Info Search.** Start with a topic on which all students have no information. Every student gets an Info Search form, which is a worksheet with questions on it. If there are ten questions on the worksheet, ten students get an answer sheet with one answer filled in. Students then play the game just like Find Someone Who. Soon all students have all the answers.

• **Find Those Who.** Students circulate about the classroom in pairs or teams searching for another pair or team that has the answers.

Grammar Skills 1
SYNONYMS & ANTONYMS

Grammar Skills 2
PARTS OF SPEECH

Grammar Skills 3
PUNCTUATION

Grammar Skills 4
SENTENCES

Grammar Skills 5
WORKING WITH WORDS

FAN-N-PICK

Teammates play a card game to respond to questions.
Roles rotate with each new question.

Setup: Each team receives a set of question or problem cards.

1 **Student #1 Fans Cards**
Student #1 holds the question cards in a fan and says, *"Pick a card, any card!"*

2 **Student #2 Picks a Card**
Student #2 picks a card, reads the question aloud, and allows five seconds of Think Time. *"Which word is the verb in the following sentence? 'Sue kicked the ball.'"*

3 **Student #3 Answers**
Student #3 answers the question. *"The verb is 'kicked.'"*

4 **Student #4 Responds**
Student #4 responds to the answer.
• For right or wrong answers: Student #4 checks the answer and then either praises or tutors the student who answered. *"That's correct! You're a true genius."* or *"I don't think that's correct; let's solve it again together."*
• For higher-level thinking questions that have no right or wrong answer: Student #4 does not check for correctness, but praises and paraphrases the thinking that went into the answer. *"Excellent response. I like the way you approached the question."*

5 **Rotate Roles**
Teammates rotate roles, one person clockwise for each new round.

Variations

• **Fan-N-Spin.** The team plays Fan-N-Pick with a random team selector spinner. After the question is read, the reader spins the spinner and the selected student answers. This keeps everyone thinking because anyone may be called on to answer at any point.

• **Pair Fan-N-Pick.** Fan-N-Pick can be played in pairs. Student #1 fans the question cards. Student #2 picks and reads a question card. Student #1 answers. Student #2 tutors or praises. Students switch roles for each new question.

Fan-N-Pick
ACTIVITIES

Grammar Skills 1
SYNONYMS & ANTONYMS

Grammar Skills 2
PARTS OF SPEECH

Grammar Skills 3
PUNCTUATION

Grammar Skills 4
SENTENCES

Grammar Skills 5
WORKING WITH WORDS

SHOWDOWN

When the Showdown Captain calls, "Showdown!" teammates all display their own answers. Teammates either celebrate or tutor, and then celebrate.

Setup: The teacher prepares questions or problems. Questions may be provided to each team as question cards that they stack facedown in the center of the table. Each student has a slate or a response board and a writing utensil.

1 **Teacher Selects Showdown Captain**
The teacher selects one student on each team to be the Showdown Captain for the first round. *"Student #4 is the first Showdown Captain. Rotate the role clockwise after each question."*

2 **Showdown Captain Reads Question**
The Showdown Captain reads the first question. If using question cards, the Showdown Captain draws the top card, reads the question, and provides Think Time. *"Think about your answer, then write it down."*

3 **Students Answer Independently**
Working alone, all students write their answers.

4 **Teammates Signal When Done**
When finished, teammates signal they're ready by turning over their response boards, putting down their markers, or giving a hand signal.

5 **Showdown Captain Calls, "Showdown"**
The Showdown Captain calls, *"Showdown!"*

6 **Teams Show Answers**
Teammates show their answers and RoundRobin state them in turn.

7 **Teams Check for Accuracy**
The Showdown Captain leads the team in checking for accuracy. *"Great. We all got the same answer."*

8 **Celebrate or Coach**
If all teammates have the correct answer, the team celebrates; if not, teammates coach the student or students with the incorrect answer, then celebrate.

9 **Rotate Captain Role**
The person on the left of the Showdown Captain becomes the Showdown Captain for the next round.

Modifications:
Rather than cards, students can play Showdown with oral questions from the teacher, or from questions on a handout or questions displayed by a projector.

Variation

- **Team Showdown.** Each team works on the same problem. When all teams have an answer, they show their team slate and compare answers with other teams. If a team misses a problem, instruction from another team or the teacher may be needed.

Showdown
ACTiViTiES

Grammar Skills 1
SYNONYMS & ANTONYMS

- Words that Are Alike...................... 23–24
- Opposites.. 28–29

Grammar Skills 2
PARTS OF SPEECH

- Action Words 35–36
- Verb Usage.................................... 49–50
- Describing Words 65–66
- Nouns...78–79
- Pronouns..96–97
- Articles.. 100–101
- Contractions.................................. 113–114

Grammar Skills 3
PUNCTUATION

- Capital Letters 130–131
- Commas 144–145
- Punctuation....................................148–149

Grammar Skills 4
SENTENCES

- Complete Sentences 156–157
- Sentence Word Order..................168–169
- Sentence Types............................ 181–182
- Action Part.....................................186–188
- Naming & Action Parts
  of a Sentence...............................189–190

Grammar Skills 5
WORKING WITH WORDS

- Writing ABC Order 196–198
- ABC Order 199–201

Mix-N-Match

Students mix, repeatedly quizzing new partners and trading cards. Afterward, they rush to find a partner with the card that matches theirs.

Setup: The teacher provides or students create pairs of matching cards.

1 Students Mix and Pair
With a card in one hand and the other hand raised, each student mixes around the room, looking for a partner with a raised hand. When they pair up, they give each other a high five. *"Pair up with another student with a raised hand. Give each other a high five and lower your hands."*

2 Partner A Asks a Question
In the pair, Partner A asks the other a question relating to his or her card. For example, *"What type of sentence ends with this punctuation mark?"*

3 Partner B Answers
Partner B answers Partner A's question. *"If it ends with an exclamation mark, it's an exclamatory sentence."*

4 Partner A Praises or Coaches
If Partner B answers correctly, Partner A praises him or her. *"That's right. Great grammar skills."* If Partner B answers incorrectly, Partner A provides the correct answer and coaches or tutors Partner B. *"I don't think that's correct. Let's look at it again."*

5 Partners Switch Roles
Partners switch roles. Partner B now asks the question and offers praise or coaches.

6 Partners Trade Cards
Before departing and looking for new partners, partners trade cards. This way, students have a new card for each new pairing.

7 Continue Quizzing and Trading
Partners split up and continue quizzing and getting quizzed by new partners. When done, they trade cards again and find a new partner.

8 Teacher Calls "Freeze"
After a sufficient time of quizzing and trading cards, the teacher calls, *"Freeze."* Students freeze, hide their cards, and think of their match.

9 Find Match
The teacher calls, *"Match."* Students search for a classmate with the matching card. When they find each other, they move to the outside of the classroom so students still searching for a match can find each other more easily.

Optional:
Teacher may post a class graph to record the time it takes for students to find their matching partners. Students try to beat their class record.

Mix-N-Match
ACTIVITIES

Grammar Skills 2
PARTS OF SPEECH

Find-N-Fix

Teammates find which answer is incorrect, then fix it.

Setup: Each teammate receives a Find-N-Fix worksheet and a set of Find-N-Fix cards.

1 Select a Captain
One student on each team is selected as the Captain. The Captain's role is to lead the team through one problem.

2 Captain Reads the Problem
The Captain reads the first set of problems and asks the team which has an incorrect answer. For example, there may be three sentences, one with incorrect punctuation.

3 Students Pick Cards
Each teammate picks one of the three Find-N-Fix Cards and holds it to his or her chin so teammates can't see the chosen card. For example, a teammate thinks the second sentence is missing commas, so he or she selects the card, *"#2 needs to be fixed."*

4 Reveal Cards
When all teammates have their cards their chins, the Captain says, *"Reveal your answer."* Students show their answers.

5 Celebrate or Coach
If all teammates have the same answer, they celebrate with a quick team cheer or handshake. Teammates coach the student(s) with the incorrect answer.

6 Teammates Correct Worksheets
Each teammate circles the incorrect answer on his or her worksheet and fixes the answer so it is correct. If necessary, students may receive help from teammates.

7 Rotate Captain Role
The Captain role is rotated one student clockwise for each new problem.

8 Continue Playing
Students continue playing until they complete the worksheet or until time is up.

Variations

- **Pair Find-N-Fix.** Students play Find-N-Fix in pairs. Partners take turns being the Captain for each set of problems.

- **Shared Find-N-Fix Worksheets.** Teams or pairs can share a worksheet. In this case, it is the Captain's job to fix the problem on the worksheet, yet the Captain must first receive consensus from teammates (or partner) before making the correction.

Page 18

FIND-N-FIX
RESPONSE CARDS

Directions: Cut out cards along the dotted line. In teams, hold up response cards indicating which answer needs to be fixed.

 # 1 needs to be fixed

 # 2 needs to be fixed

 # 3 needs to be fixed

SYNONYMS & ANTONYMS

WORDS THAT ARE ALMOST ALIKE
RallyCoach/Sage-N-Scribe

KEY IDEA

Some words have the same or almost the same meaning.

Example: The mouse is <u>small</u>. The mouse is <u>tiny</u>.

Instructions: Read the words in the box. Circle the word that has similar meaning to the first word. Take turns working with your partner to solve the problems using RallyCoach or Sage-N-Scribe.

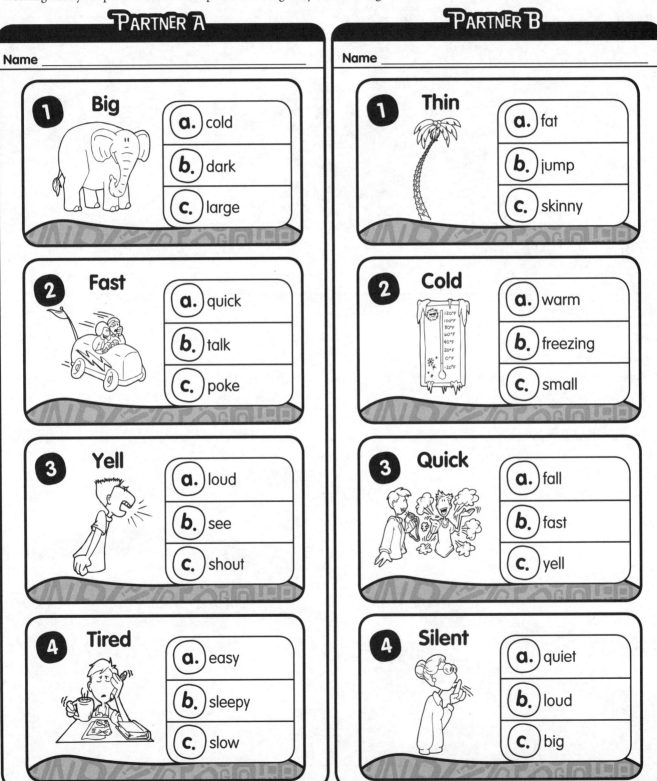

PARTNER A

Name _____

1 Big
- **a.** cold
- **b.** dark
- **c.** large

2 Fast
- **a.** quick
- **b.** talk
- **c.** poke

3 Yell
- **a.** loud
- **b.** see
- **c.** shout

4 Tired
- **a.** easy
- **b.** sleepy
- **c.** slow

PARTNER B

Name _____

1 Thin
- **a.** fat
- **b.** jump
- **c.** skinny

2 Cold
- **a.** warm
- **b.** freezing
- **c.** small

3 Quick
- **a.** fall
- **b.** fast
- **c.** yell

4 Silent
- **a.** quiet
- **b.** loud
- **c.** big

Cooperative Learning & Grammar
Kagan Publishing • 1 (800) 933-2667 • www.KaganOnline.com

SYNONYMS/ALMOST-ALIKE
Find-N-Fix

Name _____

Instructions: For each problem, find the incorrect pair. Indicate which is incorrect using your Find-N-Fix cards. When your team agrees, fix the pair by writing synonyms in the box.

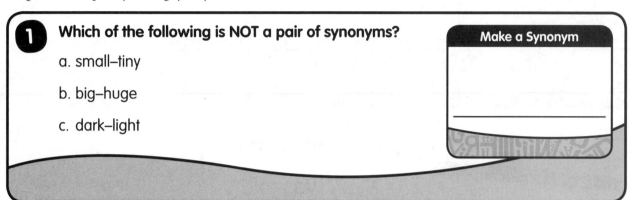

1 **Which of the following is NOT a pair of synonyms?**

a. small–tiny

b. big–huge

c. dark–light

Make a Synonym

_____

2 **Which of the following is NOT a pair of synonyms?**

a. fix–correct

b. boy–girl

c. angry–mad

Make a Synonym

_____

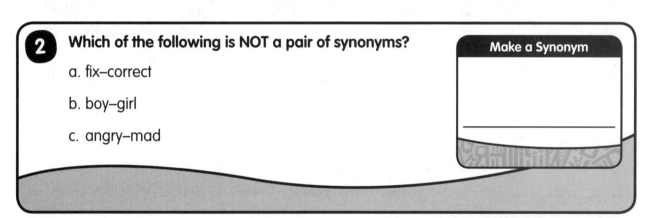

3 **Which of the following is NOT a pair of synonyms?**

a. up–down

b. father–dad

c. couch–sofa

Make a Synonym

_____

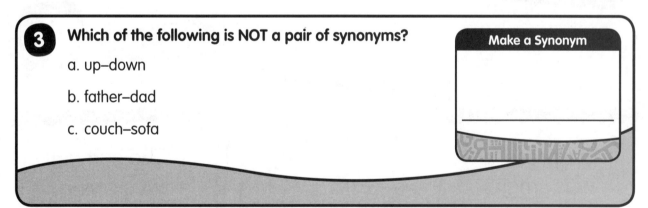

4 **Which of the following is NOT a pair of synonyms?**

a. dirt–soil

b. quiet–silent

c. friend–enemy

Make a Synonym

_____

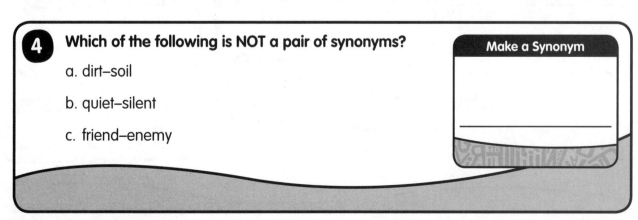

Name _____

Instructions: Pair up and take turns finding a word in the Word Bank that has similar meaning to the underlined word. Don't forget to get your partner's initials.

WORD BANK

| ill | shout | big | tiny | shut | unhappy |

Words That Are Alike

1

The gate is <u>closed</u>.

Initials

2

Mary was told not to <u>yell</u>.

Initials

3

The dog was very <u>large</u>.

Initials

4

The present was <u>small</u>.

Initials

5

John felt <u>sick</u>.

Initials

6

The <u>sad</u> girl was crying.

Initials

Cooperative Learning & Grammar
Kagan Publishing • 1 (800) 933-2667 • www.KaganOnline.com

WORDS THAT ARE ALIKE
Fan-N-Pick/Showdown

Instructions: Copy one set of cards for each team. Cut out each card along the dotted line. Give each team a set of cards to play Fan-N-Pick or Showdown.

WORDS THAT ARE ALIKE

1 Which word means the same as the underlined word?

Mom was <u>angry</u> when we were late.

a. happy
b. mad
c. crying

WORDS THAT ARE ALIKE

2 Which word means the same as the underlined word?

The <u>big</u> room was scary.

a. small
b. large
c. living

WORDS THAT ARE ALIKE

3 Which word means the same as the underlined word?

What time does the movie <u>begin</u>?

a. start
b. end
c. close

WORDS THAT ARE ALIKE

4 Which word means the same as the underlined word?

The girl had a <u>little</u> dog.

a. tiny
b. brown
c. big

WORDS THAT ARE ALIKE

5 Which word means the same as the underlined word?

The <u>quiet</u> cat was sleeping.

a. loud
b. big
c. silent

WORDS THAT ARE ALIKE

6 Which word means the same as the underlined word?

The <u>infant</u> was crying.

a. man
b. dog
c. baby

WORDS THAT ARE ALIKE
Fan-N-Pick/Showdown

Instructions: Copy one set of cards for each team. Cut out each card along the dotted line. Give each team a set of cards to play Fan-N-Pick or Showdown.

WORDS THAT ARE ALIKE

7 Which word means the same as the underlined word?

<u>Dad</u> is taking us to the park.

a. man
b. small
c. father

WORDS THAT ARE ALIKE

8 Which word means the same as the underlined word?

Please put this in the <u>trash</u>.

a. garbage
b. pretty
c. sink

WORDS THAT ARE ALIKE

9 Which word means the same as the underlined word?

The quiz was <u>easy</u>.

a. hard
b. long
c. simple

WORDS THAT ARE ALIKE

10 Which word means the same as the underlined word?

Which one do you <u>choose</u>?

a. like
b. pick
c. need

WORDS THAT ARE ALIKE

11 Which word means the same as the underlined word?

Put the sugar in the lemonade and <u>stir</u>.

a. mix
b. drink
c. enjoy

WORDS THAT ARE ALIKE

12 Which word means the same as the underlined word?

You are <u>correct</u>!

a. wrong
b. smart
c. right

Cooperative Learning & Grammar
Kagan Publishing • 1 (800) 933-2667 • www.KaganOnline.com

OPPOSITES
RallyCoach/Sage-N-Scribe

KEY IDEA Some words have the opposite meaning.

Example: The dog was <u>dirty</u>. The dog was <u>clean</u>.

Instructions: Read the word in the box. Circle the word that means the opposite of the first word. Take turns working with your partner to solve the problems using RallyCoach or Sage-N-Scribe.

PARTNER A

Name _____

1 Old
- **a.** girl
- **b.** night
- **c.** young

2 Day
- **a.** night
- **b.** black
- **c.** laugh

3 Stop
- **a.** run
- **b.** little
- **c.** go

4 Wet
- **a.** dry
- **b.** clean
- **c.** fat

PARTNER B

Name _____

1 Fat
- **a.** old
- **b.** thin
- **c.** back

2 Laugh
- **a.** high
- **b.** open
- **c.** cry

3 Open
- **a.** close
- **b.** on
- **c.** sad

4 Up
- **a.** full
- **b.** down
- **c.** empty

ANTONYMS/OPPOSITES
Find-N-Fix

Name _____

Instructions: For problem, find the incorrect pair. Indicate which is incorrect using your Find-N-Fix cards. When your team agrees, fix the pair by writing antonyms in the box.

1 Which of the following is NOT a pair of opposites?

a. all–none

b. big–little

c. rich–wealthy

Make an Antonym

_____

2 Which of the following is NOT a pair of opposites?

a. best–worst

b. choose–pick

c. stop–go

Make an Antonym

_____

3 Which of the following is NOT a pair of opposites?

a. tiny–small

b. pull–push

c. young–old

Make an Antonym

_____

4 Which of the following is NOT a pair of opposites?

a. wet–dry

b. in–out

c. dad–father

Make an Antonym

_____

Cooperative Learning & Grammar
Kagan Publishing • 1 (800) 933-2667 • www.KaganOnline.com

OPPOSITES
Find Someone Who

Name _____

Instructions: Pair up and take turns finding a word in the Word Bank that means the opposite of the underlined word. Don't forget to get your partner's initials.

WORD BANK

night   lost   closed   old   left   empty

1 The window is <u>open</u>.

Initials

2 The dog sleeps during the <u>day</u>.

Initials

3 Sam <u>won</u> the race.

Initials

4 The shoes look <u>new</u>.

Initials

5 The store is on the <u>right</u>.

Initials

6 The bowl on the table was <u>full</u>.

Initials

OPPOSITES
Fan-N-Pick/Showdown

Instructions: Copy one set of cards for each team. Cut out each card along the dotted line. Give each team a set of cards to play Fan-N-Pick or Showdown.

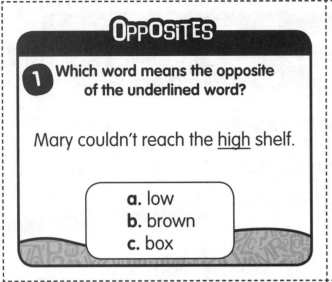

OPPOSITES

1 Which word means the opposite of the underlined word?

Mary couldn't reach the <u>high</u> shelf.

- **a.** low
- **b.** brown
- **c.** box

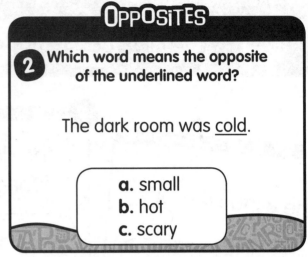

OPPOSITES

2 Which word means the opposite of the underlined word?

The dark room was <u>cold</u>.

- **a.** small
- **b.** hot
- **c.** scary

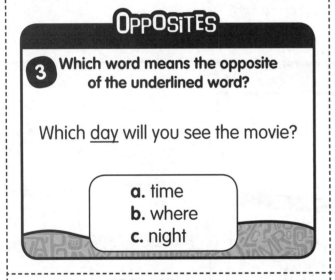

OPPOSITES

3 Which word means the opposite of the underlined word?

Which <u>day</u> will you see the movie?

- **a.** time
- **b.** where
- **c.** night

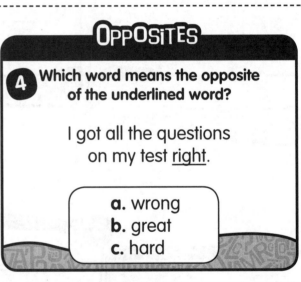

OPPOSITES

4 Which word means the opposite of the underlined word?

I got all the questions on my test <u>right</u>.

- **a.** wrong
- **b.** great
- **c.** hard

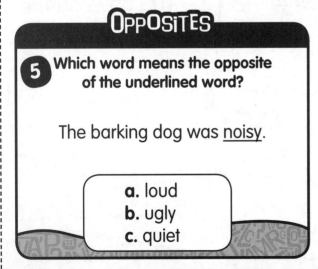

OPPOSITES

5 Which word means the opposite of the underlined word?

The barking dog was <u>noisy</u>.

- **a.** loud
- **b.** ugly
- **c.** quiet

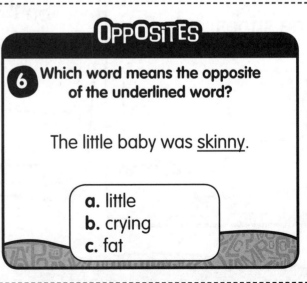

OPPOSITES

6 Which word means the opposite of the underlined word?

The little baby was <u>skinny</u>.

- **a.** little
- **b.** crying
- **c.** fat

Cooperative Learning & Grammar
Kagan Publishing • 1 (800) 933-2667 • www.KaganOnline.com

Fan-N-Pick/Showdown

Instructions: Copy one set of cards for each team. Cut out each card along the dotted line. Give each team a set of cards to play Fan-N-Pick or Showdown.

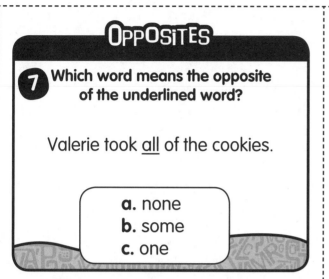

OPPOSITES

7 Which word means the opposite of the underlined word?

Valerie took <u>all</u> of the cookies.

a. none
b. some
c. one

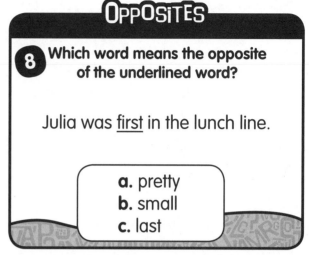

OPPOSITES

8 Which word means the opposite of the underlined word?

Julia was <u>first</u> in the lunch line.

a. pretty
b. small
c. last

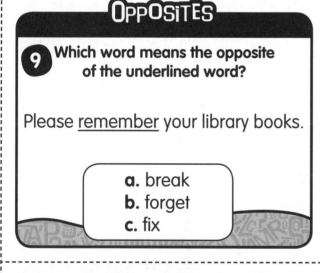

OPPOSITES

9 Which word means the opposite of the underlined word?

Please <u>remember</u> your library books.

a. break
b. forget
c. fix

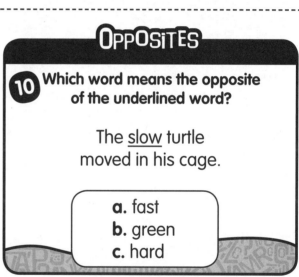

OPPOSITES

10 Which word means the opposite of the underlined word?

The <u>slow</u> turtle moved in his cage.

a. fast
b. green
c. hard

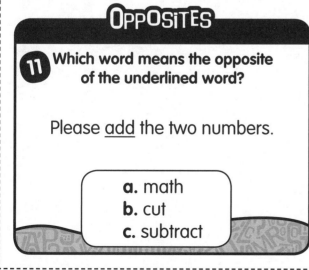

OPPOSITES

11 Which word means the opposite of the underlined word?

Please <u>add</u> the two numbers.

a. math
b. cut
c. subtract

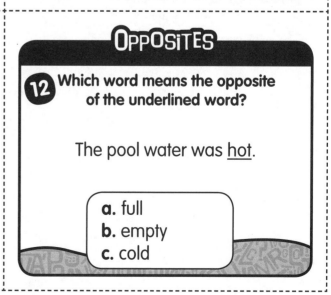

OPPOSITES

12 Which word means the opposite of the underlined word?

The pool water was <u>hot</u>.

a. full
b. empty
c. cold

Cooperative Learning & Grammar
Kagan Publishing • 1 (800) 933-2667 • www.KaganOnline.com   Synonyms & Antonyms   **29**

Grammar Skills 2

PARTS OF SPEECH

Action Words
RallyCoach/Sage-N-Scribe

Instructions: Choose a verb from the Word Bank to correctly complete the sentences below. Take turns working with your partner to solve the problems using RallyCoach or Sage-N-Scribe.

PARTNER A   **PARTNER B**

WORD BANK

(flies)   (asked)   (built)   (write)   (works)   (zipped)

Name _____   Name _____

1 Sheldon _____ a question at the meeting.

_____

- - - - - - - - - - - - - - -

_____

1 Kyle _____ a house out of his wooden blocks.

_____

- - - - - - - - - - - - - - -

_____

2 The students will _____ a poem during writer's workshop.

_____

- - - - - - - - - - - - - - -

_____

2 My dad _____ my jacket up before going outside.

_____

- - - - - - - - - - - - - - -

_____

3 My mom _____ at the local grocery store.

_____

- - - - - - - - - - - - - - -

_____

3 The bird _____ to find worms for her family.

_____

- - - - - - - - - - - - - - -

_____

Cooperative Learning & Grammar
Kagan Publishing • 1 (800) 933-2667 • www.KaganOnline.com

Name _____

Instructions: Pair up and take turns finding a word in the Word Bank that matches the action in the picture. Don't forget to get your partner's initials.

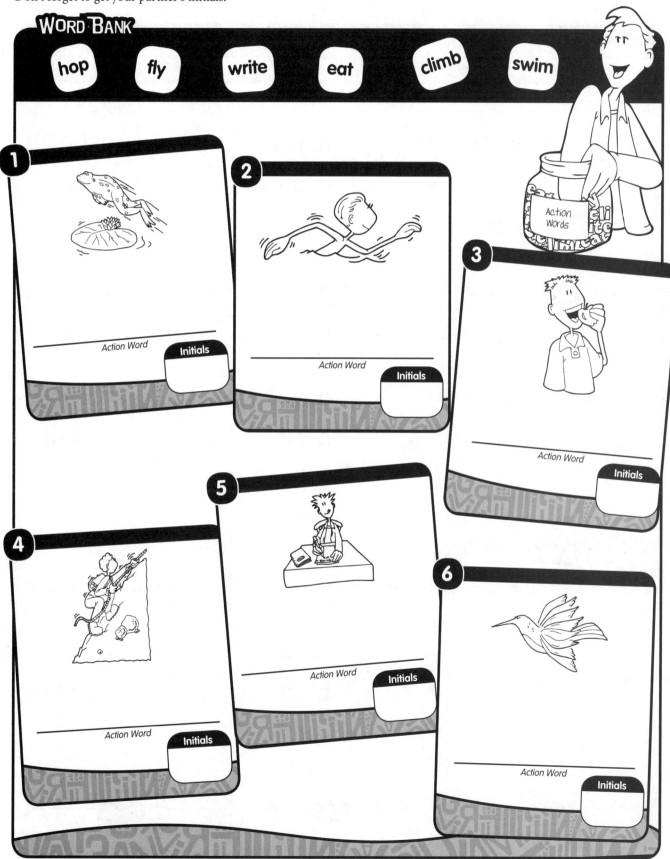

WORD BANK

hop · fly · write · eat · climb · swim

1. Action Word _____ Initials
2. Action Word _____ Initials
3. Action Word _____ Initials
4. Action Word _____ Initials
5. Action Word _____ Initials
6. Action Word _____ Initials

Action Words
Find Someone Who

Instructions: Pair up and take turns determining which action word describes the picture. Don't forget to get your partner's initials.

a. jump b. run c. kick	a. find b. swim c. clap	a. brush b. dive c. eat
Initials	*Initials*	*Initials*
a. grab b. dance c. run	a. yell b. sit c. jump	a. run b. dive c. jump
Initials	*Initials*	*Initials*
a. listen b. run c. eat	a. jump b. sit c. talk	a. dive b. listen c. eat
Initials	*Initials*	*Initials*

Cooperative Learning & Grammar
Kagan Publishing • 1 (800) 933-2667 • www.KaganOnline.com

Instructions: Copy one set of cards for each team. Cut out each card along the dotted line. Give each team a set of cards to play Fan-N-Pick or Showdown.

ACTION WORDS

1

What is the action word in the sentence?

She ran to the store.

ACTION WORDS

2

What is the action word in the sentence?

The dog ran.

ACTION WORDS

3

What is the action word in the sentence?

Jan kicked the ball.

ACTION WORDS

4

What is the action word in the sentence?

The frog hopped to land.

ACTION WORDS

5

What is the action word in the sentence?

Sue swam in the lake.

ACTION WORDS

6

What is the action word in the sentence?

My mom cooked dinner.

Instructions: Copy one set of cards for each team. Cut out each card along the dotted line. Give each team a set of cards to play Fan-N-Pick or Showdown.

ACTION WORDS

7

What is the action word in the sentence?

Paul drew a picture.

ACTION WORDS

8

What is the action word in the sentence?

Please chew your food.

ACTION WORDS

9

What is the action word in the sentence?

My dad drove the car.

ACTION WORDS

10

What is the action word in the sentence?

The cat climbed the tree.

ACTION WORDS

11

What is the action word in the sentence?

The baby sleeps in the crib.

ACTION WORDS

12

What is the action word in the sentence?

I cut the paper.

Cooperative Learning & Grammar
Kagan Publishing • 1 (800) 933-2667 • www.KaganOnline.com

Action Words
Quiz-Quiz-Trade

Instructions: Cut out each card along the dotted line. Then fold each card in half so the question is on one side and the answer is on the back. Glue or tape the cards together to keep the answers and questions on opposite sides.

Action Words
1 Question

Which action word best fits the picture?

a. jump
b. run
c. swim

Action Words
1 Answer

c. swim

Action Words
2 Question

Which action word best fits the picture?

a. sing
b. play
c. write

Action Words
2 Answer

c. write

Action Words
3 Question

Which action word best fits the picture?

a. shop
b. talk
c. eat

Action Words
3 Answer

a. shop

ACTION WORDS
Quiz-Quiz-Trade

Instructions: Cut out each card along the dotted line. Then fold each card in half so the question is on one side and the answer is on the back. Glue or tape the cards together to keep the answers and questions on opposite sides.

ACTION WORDS
Question

4

Which action word best fits the picture?

a. fly
b. buy
c. wave

ACTION WORDS
Answer

4

c. wave

ACTION WORDS
Question

5

Which action word best fits the picture?

a. clean
b. brush
c. bark

ACTION WORDS
Answer

5

b. brush

ACTION WORDS
Question

6

Which action word best fits the picture?

a. jump
b. eat
c. rest

ACTION WORDS
Answer

6

b. eat

Cooperative Learning & Grammar
Kagan Publishing • 1 (800) 933-2667 • www.KaganOnline.com

Instructions: Cut out each card along the dotted line. Then fold each card in half so the question is on one side and the answer is on the back. Glue or tape the cards together to keep the answers and questions on opposite sides.

ACTION WORDS
7 Question

Which action word best fits the picture?

a. climb
b. sit
c. run

ACTION WORDS
7 Answer

a. climb

ACTION WORDS
8 Question

Which action word best fits the picture?

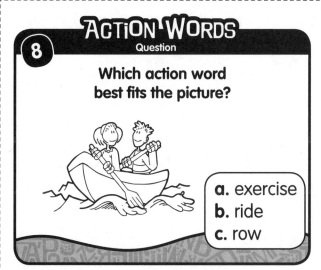

a. exercise
b. ride
c. row

ACTION WORDS
8 Answer

c. row

ACTION WORDS
9 Question

Which action word best fits the picture?

a. wash
b. row
c. dive

ACTION WORDS
9 Answer

c. dive

ACTION WORDS
Quiz-Quiz-Trade

Instructions: Cut out each card along the dotted line. Then fold each card in half so the question is on one side and the answer is on the back. Glue or tape the cards together to keep the answers and questions on opposite sides.

10 ACTION WORDS
Question

Which action word best fits the picture?

a. clap
b. sing
c. laugh

10 ACTION WORDS
Answer

a. clap

11 ACTION WORDS
Question

Which action word best fits the picture?

a. dance
b. cheer
c. argue

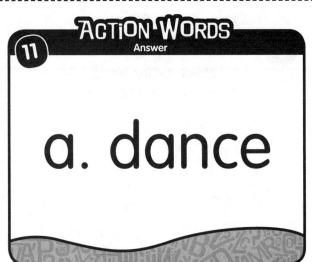

11 ACTION WORDS
Answer

a. dance

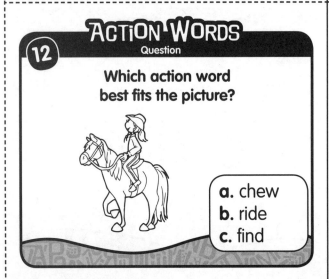

12 ACTION WORDS
Question

Which action word best fits the picture?

a. chew
b. ride
c. find

12 ACTION WORDS
Answer

b. ride

Cooperative Learning & Grammar
Kagan Publishing • 1 (800) 933-2667 • www.KaganOnline.com

ACTION WORDS
Quiz-Quiz-Trade

Instructions: Cut out each card along the dotted line. Then fold each card in half so the question is on one side and the answer is on the back. Glue or tape the cards together to keep the answers and questions on opposite sides.

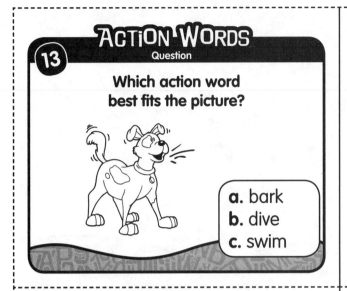

ACTION WORDS
Question

13

Which action word best fits the picture?

a. bark
b. dive
c. swim

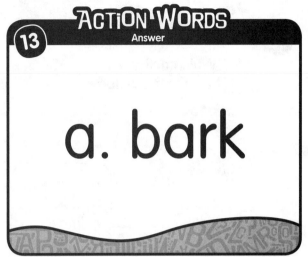

ACTION WORDS
Answer

13

a. bark

ACTION WORDS
Question

14

Which action word best fits the picture?

a. wave
b. clap
c. sing

ACTION WORDS
Answer

14

c. sing

ACTION WORDS
Question

15

Which action word best fits the picture?

a. yell
b. dance
c. clean

ACTION WORDS
Answer

15

c. clean

Instructions: Cut out each card along the dotted line. Then fold each card in half so the question is on one side and the answer is on the back. Glue or tape the cards together to keep the answers and questions on opposite sides.

ACTION WORDS
16 Question

Which action word best fits the picture?

a. sell
b. talk
c. lift

ACTION WORDS
16 Answer

c. lift

ACTION WORDS
17 Question

Which action word best fits the picture?

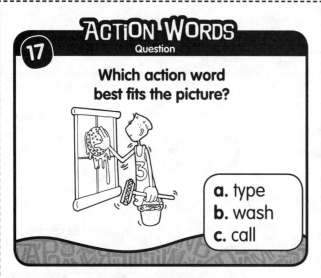

a. type
b. wash
c. call

ACTION WORDS
17 Answer

b. wash

ACTION WORDS
18 Question

Which action word best fits the picture?

a. play
b. roll
c. climb

ACTION WORDS
18 Answer

a. play

Cooperative Learning & Grammar
Kagan Publishing • 1 (800) 933-2667 • www.KaganOnline.com

Instructions: Cut out each card along the dotted line. Then fold each card in half so the question is on one side and the answer is on the back. Glue or tape the cards together to keep the answers and questions on opposite sides.

19

ACTION WORDS
Question

Which action word best fits the picture?

a. drive
b. sail
c. read

19

ACTION WORDS
Answer

c. read

20

ACTION WORDS
Question

Which action word best fits the picture?

a.
b.
c.

20

ACTION WORDS
Answer

21

ACTION WORDS
Question

Which action word best fits the picture?

a.
b.
c.

21

ACTION WORDS
Answer

USING ACTION WORDS
RallyCoach/Sage-N-Scribe

Instructions: In the sentences below, choose the word that correctly completes the sentence. Take turns working with your partner to solve the problems using RallyCoach or Sage-N-Scribe.

PARTNER A

Name _____

1 Gordon _____ together his train track.
a. putting
b. put
c. putted

2 Tomorrow we will go _____ at the pool.
a. swimming
b. swam
c. swims

3 The young boy _____ in the gym.
a. yelled
b. yell
c. yelling

4 Last night, the baby _____ very loudly.
a. cries
b. cried
c. crying

5 The car _____ running ten minutes ago.
a. stops
b. stopping
c. stopped

PARTNER B

Name _____

1 The player _____ the winning goal yesterday.
a. kicking
b. kicks
c. kicked

2 The phone is _____ in the kitchen.
a. ringing
b. rang
c. rings

3 The water was _____ down the street.
a. rushed
b. rushes
c. rushing

4 Mom will _____ the car in the morning.
a. cleans
b. clean
c. cleaning

5 The monkey wants to _____ a banana.
a. pick
b. picking
c. picked

Cooperative Learning & Grammar
Kagan Publishing • 1 (800) 933-2667 • www.KaganOnline.com

USING ACTION WORDS
RallyCoach/Sage-N-Scribe

Instructions: Use the words from the box to complete the sentences below. Each word will be used once. Take turns working with your partner to solve the problems using RallyCoach or Sage-N-Scribe.

PARTNER A

Name _____

1 (gave) (give) (giving)

Kolby _____ his mother a present.

Max is_____ the dog a bath.

I will _____ you an apple for lunch.

2 (climbs) (climbing) (climbed)

Najem is _____ the stairs.

The squirrel _____ to the top of the tree.

Yesterday, I _____ up steep hills.

3 (run) (ran) (runs)

Please do not _____ in the hallway.

Lynn _____ faster than a train.

I _____ the mile race at the track meet.

PARTNER B

Name _____

1 (plays) (played) (playing)

I was _____ with my toy cars in the sand.

Preston _____ outside and got all muddy.

Clint _____ the guitar and sings.

2 (talks) (talking) (talked)

Kyle _____ too loudly in the library.

Michele _____ on the phone to her dad.

Stefanie is_____ about her new book.

3 (reads) (read) (reading)

Shawna is _____ an adventure book.

Mrs. McKoy loves to _____ to her students.

Brandon _____ in an excited voice.

Is, Am, Are
Find Someone Who

Instructions: Pair up and take turns filling in the blank with "is," "am," or "are." Don't forget to get your partner's initials.

1 I _____ going to the pool.
a. is
b. am
c. are

Initials

2 What _____ your address?
a. is
b. am
c. are

Initials

3 Where _____ you going?
a. is
b. am
c. are

Initials

4 I _____ getting a dog.
a. is
b. am
c. are

Initials

5 How _____ your foot?
a. is
b. am
c. are

Initials

6 When _____ you coming home?
a. is
b. am
c. are

Initials

7 Polly _____ running late.
a. is
b. am
c. are

Initials

8 How many crayons _____ in the box?
a. is
b. am
c. are

Initials

9 How _____ I going to get it home?
a. is
b. am
c. are

Initials

Cooperative Learning & Grammar
Kagan Publishing • 1 (800) 933-2667 • www.KaganOnline.com

Name _____

Instructions: Pair up and take turns finding the word in the Word Bank that is past tense of the action word. Don't forget to get your partner's initials.

WORD BANK

ran   ate   drew   drove   swam   wrote

1 run

_____
Past Tense

Initials

2 swim

_____
Past Tense

Initials

3 write

_____
Past Tense

Initials

5 draw

_____
Past Tense

Initials

4 drive

_____
Past Tense

Initials

6 eat

_____
Past Tense

Initials

PAST & PRESENT ACTION WORDS
Find Someone Who

Instructions: Pair up and take turns placing a word from the Word Bank in the correct category below. Don't forget to get your partner's initials.

WORD BANK

dive   jump   walk   blow   ran   came
wrote   swam   run   walked   blew   dove   jumped
write   come   eat   swim   ate

Past		Present	
1. _____	Initials	1. _____	Initials
2. _____	Initials	2. _____	Initials
3. _____	Initials	3. _____	Initials
4. _____	Initials	4. _____	Initials
5. _____	Initials	5. _____	Initials
6. _____	Initials	6. _____	Initials
7. _____	Initials	7. _____	Initials
8. _____	Initials	8. _____	Initials
9. _____	Initials	9. _____	Initials

Cooperative Learning & Grammar
Kagan Publishing • 1 (800) 933-2667 • www.KaganOnline.com

VERB USAGE
Fan-N-Pick/Showdown

Instructions: Copy one set of cards for each team. Cut out each card along the dotted line. Give each team a set of cards to play Fan-N-Pick or Showdown.

VERB USAGE

1 Fill in the blank by using "was" or "were" to complete the sentence.

When _____ you home?

VERB USAGE

2 Fill in the blank by using "was" or "were" to complete the sentence.

The girl _____ ten years old.

VERB USAGE

3 Fill in the blank by using "was" or "were" to complete the sentence.

How long _____ you at the game?

VERB USAGE

4 Fill in the blank by using "was" or "were" to complete the sentence.

Ben and Jenny _____ at the pizza place last night.

VERB USAGE

5 Fill in the blank by using "Was" or "Were" to complete the sentence.

_____ Jimmy at school today?

VERB USAGE

6 Fill in the blank by using "was" or "were" to complete the sentence.

How _____ your lunch?

Instructions: Copy one set of cards for each team. Cut out each card along the dotted line. Give each team a set of cards to play Fan-N-Pick or Showdown.

VERB USAGE

7 Fill in the blank by using "was" or "were" to complete the sentence.

We _____ going to build a campfire.

VERB USAGE

8 Fill in the blank by using "was" or "were" to complete the sentence.

What _____ you doing with the crayon?

VERB USAGE

9 Fill in the blank by using "was" or "were" to complete the sentence.

Jackie said the book _____ good.

VERB USAGE

10 Fill in the blank by using "was" or "were" to complete the sentence.

How big _____ the bear?

VERB USAGE

11 Fill in the blank by using "was" or "were" to complete the sentence.

My sister got a job when she _____ 16 years old.

VERB USAGE

12 Fill in the blank by using "was" or "were" to complete the sentence.

When _____ your last doctor visit?

Cooperative Learning & Grammar
Kagan Publishing • 1 (800) 933-2667 • www.KaganOnline.com

IRREGULAR ACTION WORDS
Mix-N-Match

Instructions: Cut out the cards on the dotted line. Give one card to each student. Distribute cards in sequence so for every student with a Past Tense card, there is a student with a matching Present Tense card.

IRREGULAR ACTION WORDS

What is the *past* tense of the action word below?

give

Present Tense

IRREGULAR ACTION WORDS

What is the *present* tense of the action word below?

gave

Past Tense

IRREGULAR ACTION WORDS

What is the *past* tense of the action word below?

run

Present Tense

IRREGULAR ACTION WORDS

What is the *present* tense of the action word below?

ran

Past Tense

IRREGULAR ACTION WORDS

What is the *past* tense of the action word below?

swim

Present Tense

IRREGULAR ACTION WORDS

What is the *present* tense of the action word below?

swam

Past Tense

IRREGULAR ACTION WORDS

What is the *past* tense of the action word below?

eat

Present Tense

IRREGULAR ACTION WORDS

What is the *present* tense of the action word below?

ate

Past Tense

IRREGULAR ACTION WORDS
Mix-N-Match

Instructions: Cut out the cards on the dotted line. Give one card to each student. Distribute cards in sequence so for every student with a Past Tense card, there is a student with a matching Present Tense card.

IRREGULAR ACTION WORDS

What is the *past* tense of the action word below?

see

Present Tense

IRREGULAR ACTION WORDS

What is the *present* tense of the action word below?

saw

Past Tense

IRREGULAR ACTION WORDS

What is the *past* tense of the action word below?

tell

Present Tense

IRREGULAR ACTION WORDS

What is the *present* tense of the action word below?

told

Past Tense

IRREGULAR ACTION WORDS

What is the *past* tense of the action word below?

drink

Present Tense

IRREGULAR ACTION WORDS

What is the *present* tense of the action word below?

drank

Past Tense

IRREGULAR ACTION WORDS

What is the *past* tense of the action word below?

get

Present Tense

IRREGULAR ACTION WORDS

What is the *present* tense of the action word below?

got

Past Tense

Cooperative Learning & Grammar
Kagan Publishing • 1 (800) 933-2667 • www.KaganOnline.com

Instructions: Cut out the cards on the dotted line. Give one card to each student. Distribute cards in sequence so for every student with a Past Tense card, there is a student with a matching Present Tense card.

IRREGULAR ACTION WORDS

What is the _past_ tense of the action word below?

fall

Present Tense

IRREGULAR ACTION WORDS

What is the _present_ tense of the action word below?

fell

Past Tense

IRREGULAR ACTION WORDS

What is the _past_ tense of the action word below?

draw

Present Tense

IRREGULAR ACTION WORDS

What is the _present_ tense of the action word below?

drew

Past Tense

IRREGULAR ACTION WORDS

What is the _past_ tense of the action word below?

fight

Present Tense

IRREGULAR ACTION WORDS

What is the _present_ tense of the action word below?

fought

Past Tense

IRREGULAR ACTION WORDS

What is the _past_ tense of the action word below?

grow

Present Tense

IRREGULAR ACTION WORDS

What is the _present_ tense of the action word below?

grew

Past Tense

IRREGULAR ACTION WORDS
Mix-N-Match

Instructions: Cut out the cards on the dotted line. Give one card to each student. Distribute cards in sequence so for every student with a Past Tense card, there is a student with a matching Present Tense card.

IRREGULAR ACTION WORDS

What is the *past* tense of the action word below?

hear

Present Tense

IRREGULAR ACTION WORDS

What is the *present* tense of the action word below?

heard

Past Tense

IRREGULAR ACTION WORDS

What is the *past* tense of the action word below?

catch

Present Tense

IRREGULAR ACTION WORDS

What is the *present* tense of the action word below?

caught

Past Tense

IRREGULAR ACTION WORDS

What is the *past* tense of the action word below?

dive

Present Tense

IRREGULAR ACTION WORDS

What is the *present* tense of the action word below?

dove

Past Tense

IRREGULAR ACTION WORDS

What is the *past* tense of the action word below?

know

Present Tense

IRREGULAR ACTION WORDS

What is the *present* tense of the action word below?

knew

Past Tense

Cooperative Learning & Grammar
Kagan Publishing • 1 (800) 933-2667 • www.KaganOnline.com

ACTION WORDS
Quiz-Quiz-Trade

Instructions: Cut out each card along the dotted line. Then fold each card in half so the question is on one side and the answer is on the back. Glue or tape the cards together to keep the answers and questions on opposite sides.

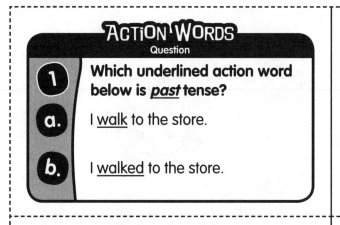

ACTION WORDS
Question

1 Which underlined action word below is *past* tense?

a. I <u>walk</u> to the store.

b. I <u>walked</u> to the store.

ACTION WORDS
Answer

1 **b.**

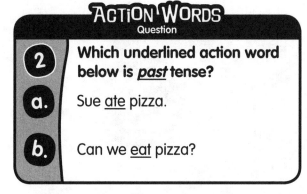

ACTION WORDS
Question

2 Which underlined action word below is *past* tense?

a. Sue <u>ate</u> pizza.

b. Can we <u>eat</u> pizza?

ACTION WORDS
Answer

2 **a.**

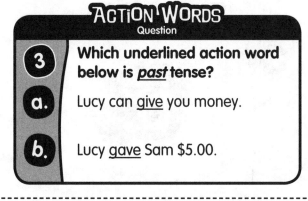

ACTION WORDS
Question

3 Which underlined action word below is *past* tense?

a. Lucy can <u>give</u> you money.

b. Lucy <u>gave</u> Sam $5.00.

ACTION WORDS
Answer

3 **b.**

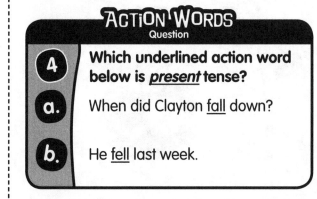

ACTION WORDS
Question

4 Which underlined action word below is *present* tense?

a. When did Clayton <u>fall</u> down?

b. He <u>fell</u> last week.

ACTION WORDS
Answer

4 **a.**

Action Words
Quiz-Quiz-Trade

Instructions: Cut out each card along the dotted line. Then fold each card in half so the question is on one side and the answer is on the back. Glue or tape the cards together to keep the answers and questions on opposite sides.

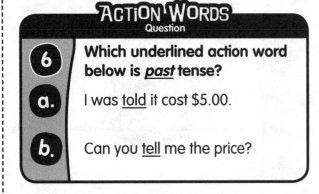

ACTION WORDS
Question

5 Which underlined action word below is *past* tense?

a. Can you <u>swim</u> a mile?

b. Joe <u>swam</u> three miles.

ACTION WORDS
Answer

5 **b.**

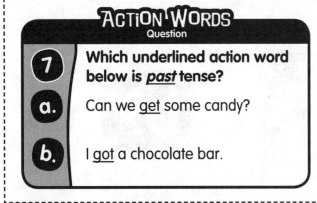

ACTION WORDS
Question

6 Which underlined action word below is *past* tense?

a. I was <u>told</u> it cost $5.00.

b. Can you <u>tell</u> me the price?

ACTION WORDS
Answer

6 **a.**

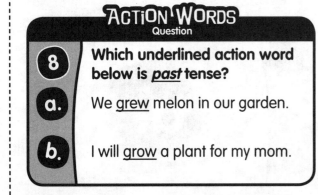

ACTION WORDS
Question

7 Which underlined action word below is *past* tense?

a. Can we <u>get</u> some candy?

b. I <u>got</u> a chocolate bar.

ACTION WORDS
Answer

7 **b.**

ACTION WORDS
Question

8 Which underlined action word below is *past* tense?

a. We <u>grew</u> melon in our garden.

b. I will <u>grow</u> a plant for my mom.

ACTION WORDS
Answer

8 **a.**

Cooperative Learning & Grammar
Kagan Publishing • 1 (800) 933-2667 • www.KaganOnline.com

Action Words
Quiz-Quiz-Trade

Instructions: Cut out each card along the dotted line. Then fold each card in half so the question is on one side and the answer is on the back. Glue or tape the cards together to keep the answers and questions on opposite sides.

Action Words
Question

9

Which underlined action word below is _past_ tense?

a. I <u>knew</u> the answer.

b. Do you <u>know</u> the answer?

Action Words
Answer

9

a.

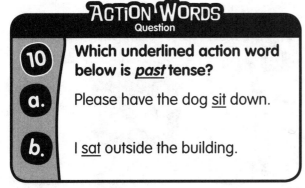

Action Words
Question

10

Which underlined action word below is _past_ tense?

a. Please have the dog <u>sit</u> down.

b. I <u>sat</u> outside the building.

Action Words
Answer

10

b.

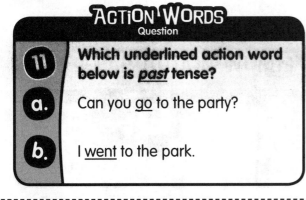

Action Words
Question

11

Which underlined action word below is _past_ tense?

a. Can you <u>go</u> to the party?

b. I <u>went</u> to the park.

Action Words
Answer

11

b.

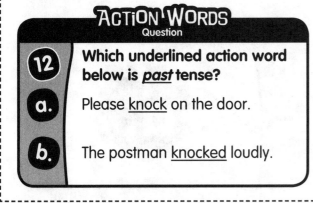

Action Words
Question

12

Which underlined action word below is _past_ tense?

a. Please <u>knock</u> on the door.

b. The postman <u>knocked</u> loudly.

Action Words
Answer

12

b.

Action Words
Quiz-Quiz-Trade

Instructions: Cut out each card along the dotted line. Then fold each card in half so the question is on one side and the answer is on the back. Glue or tape the cards together to keep the answers and questions on opposite sides.

ACTION WORDS
Question

13 Which underlined action word below is *present* tense?

a. The frog <u>jumped</u> away.

b. The frog <u>jumps</u>.

ACTION WORDS
Question

14 Which underlined action word below is *present* tense?

a. My dad <u>flew</u> in a plane.

b. My dad is <u>flying</u> in a plane.

ACTION WORDS
Question

15 Which underlined action word below is *present* tense?

a. Mrs. Smith <u>wrote</u> a letter.

b. Mrs. Smith is <u>writing</u> a letter.

ACTION WORDS
Question

16 Which underlined action word below is *present* tense?

a. My mom can <u>see</u> us out the window.

b. My mom <u>saw</u> me jump.

Cooperative Learning & Grammar
Kagan Publishing • 1 (800) 933-2667 • www.KaganOnline.com

ACTION WORDS
Quiz-Quiz-Trade

Instructions: Cut out each card along the dotted line. Then fold each card in half so the question is on one side and the answer is on the back. Glue or tape the cards together to keep the answers and questions on opposite sides.

ACTION WORDS
Question

17

Which underlined action word below is *present* tense?

a. I <u>took</u> a long bath.

b. My brother <u>drank</u> two cups of milk.

ACTION WORDS
Answer

17

a.

ACTION WORDS
Question

18

Which underlined action word below is *present* tense?

a. I <u>heard</u> Jack was sick.

b. Do you <u>hear</u> the water running?

ACTION WORDS
Answer

18

b.

ACTION WORDS
Question

19

Which underlined action word below is *present* tense?

a. Please <u>chew</u> your food.

b. I <u>chewed</u> the food.

ACTION WORDS
Answer

19

a.

ACTION WORDS
Question

20

Which underlined action word below is *present* tense?

a. The baby is <u>sleeping</u>.

b. He <u>slept</u> for three hours.

ACTION WORDS
Answer

20

a.

ACTION WORDS
Quiz-Quiz-Trade

Instructions: Cut out each card along the dotted line. Then fold each card in half so the question is on one side and the answer is on the back. Glue or tape the cards together to keep the answers and questions on opposite sides.

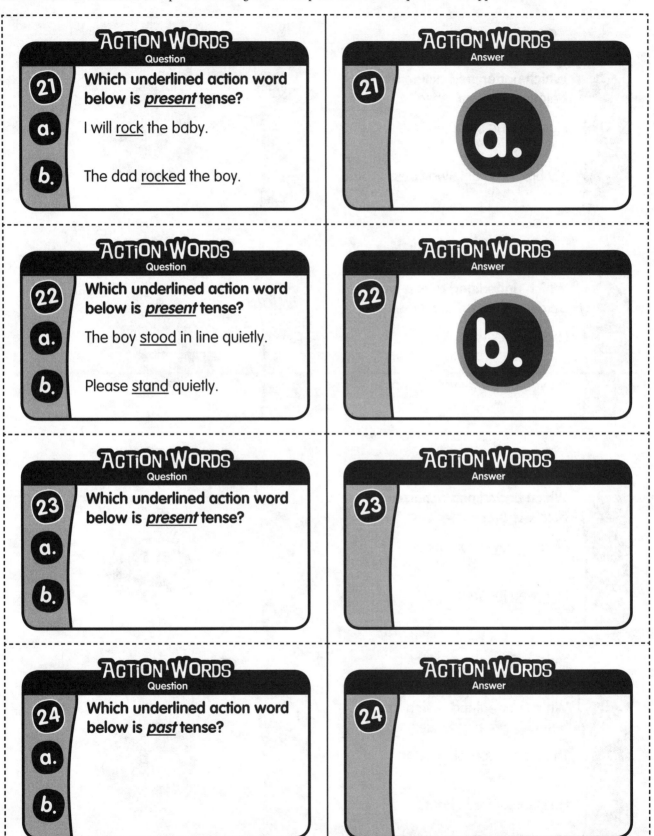

ACTION WORDS
Question

21 Which underlined action word below is *present* tense?

a. I will <u>rock</u> the baby.

b. The dad <u>rocked</u> the boy.

ACTION WORDS
Answer

21 **a.**

ACTION WORDS
Question

22 Which underlined action word below is *present* tense?

a. The boy <u>stood</u> in line quietly.

b. Please <u>stand</u> quietly.

ACTION WORDS
Answer

22 **b.**

ACTION WORDS
Question

23 Which underlined action word below is *present* tense?

a.

b.

ACTION WORDS
Answer

23

ACTION WORDS
Question

24 Which underlined action word below is *past* tense?

a.

b.

ACTION WORDS
Answer

24

Cooperative Learning & Grammar
Kagan Publishing • 1 (800) 933-2667 • www.KaganOnline.com

DESCRIBING WORDS
RallyCoach/Sage-N-Scribe

Instructions: Choose the best adjective from the box to correctly complete the sentences below. Take turns working with your partner to solve the problems using RallyCoach or Sage-N-Scribe.

PARTNER A	PARTNER B

Name _____   Name _____

long green dirty	sturdy fluffy fresh

1 The dog has a _____ tail.

1 The _____ blanket helps the baby go to sleep.

2 The _____ dishes need to be cleaned and put away.

2 The lamp is on the _____ desk in the office.

3 The living room has a _____ rug.

3 Karen picks _____ strawberries from the field.

DESCRIBING WORDS
RallyCoach/Sage-N-Scribe

KEY IDEA — Describing words are words that tell more about a noun.

Example: The <u>small</u> girl ran to her mother. Small describes the girl.

Instructions: In the sentences below, add an adjective in the blank to make the sentence more descriptive. Take turns working with your partner to solve the problems using RallyCoach or Sage-N-Scribe.

PARTNER A		PARTNER B	
Name _____		Name _____	
1	The _____ bear ran through the woods.	1	We saw lots of _____ sand on the beach.
2	The _____ boy played in the sand.	2	The _____ lion walked around his cage.
3	The wind blew the _____ kite in the air.	3	A _____ man was feeding the monkeys.
4	The _____ pumpkin sat on the porch.	4	The _____ apple was sitting on the desk.
5	My mom bought me _____ ice cream.	5	The _____ clouds filled the sky.

Cooperative Learning & Grammar
Kagan Publishing • 1 (800) 933-2667 • www.KaganOnline.com

DESCRIBING WORDS
Find Someone Who

Instructions: Pair up and take turns determining which word describes the picture. Don't forget to get your partner's initials.

1
a. hot
b. cold
c. old

Initials

2
a. small
b. soft
c. huge

Initials

3
a. loud
b. smooth
c. young

Initials

4
a. long
b. hot
c. smart

Initials

5
a. sad
b. scared
c. happy

Initials

6
a. wet
b. dry
c. colorful

Initials

7
a. cloudy
b. bright
c. young

Initials

8
a. round
b. bouncy
c. soft

Initials

9
a. young
b. weak
c. bumpy

Initials

DESCRIBING WORDS
Find Someone Who

Name _____

Instructions: Pair up and take turns finding a word from the Word Bank that best describes the picture. Don't forget to get your partner's initials.

WORD BANK

hot　　wet　　cold　　furry　　fragile　　sharp

Cooperative Learning & Grammar
Kagan Publishing • 1 (800) 933-2667 • www.KaganOnline.com

Instructions: Copy one set of cards for each team. Cut out each card along the dotted line. Give each team a set of cards to play Fan-N-Pick or Showdown.

DESCRIBING WORDS

1

Add a describing
word in the blank.

Jimmy's _____ frog
hopped away.

DESCRIBING WORDS

2

Add a describing
word in the blank.

The _____
bear ran.

DESCRIBING WORDS

3

Add a describing
word in the blank.

The _____ sky
filled with clouds.

DESCRIBING WORDS

4

Add a describing
word in the blank.

The _____ ice
cream melted.

DESCRIBING WORDS

5

Add a describing
word in the blank.

I have a _____
goldfish.

DESCRIBING WORDS

6

Add a describing
word in the blank.

The _____ apple
fell on the floor.

Instructions: Copy one set of cards for each team. Cut out each card along the dotted line. Give each team a set of cards to play Fan-N-Pick or Showdown.

DESCRIBING WORDS

7

Add a describing
word in the blank.

The _____ rug
had a stain.

DESCRIBING WORDS

8

Add a describing
word in the blank.

Susie ate the
_____ cookies.

DESCRIBING WORDS

9

Add a describing
word in the blank.

Please put away
your _____ shoes.

DESCRIBING WORDS

10

Add a describing
word in the blank.

The _____ rabbit
hopped away.

DESCRIBING WORDS

11

Add a describing
word in the blank.

The bed was
very _____.

DESCRIBING WORDS

12

Add a describing
word in the blank.

The _____ dish was
in the sink.

DESCRIBING WORDS
Quiz-Quiz-Trade

Instructions: Cut out each card along the dotted line. Then fold each card in half so the question is on one side and the answer is on the back. Glue or tape the cards together to keep the answers and questions on opposite sides.

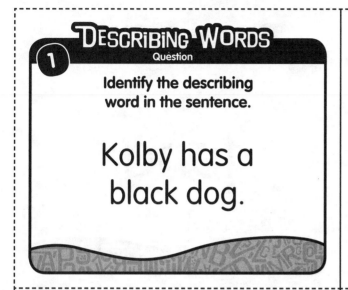

DESCRIBING WORDS
Question
1

Identify the describing word in the sentence.

Kolby has a black dog.

DESCRIBING WORDS
Answer
1

black

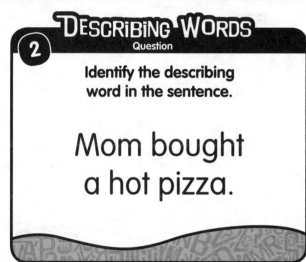

DESCRIBING WORDS
Question
2

Identify the describing word in the sentence.

Mom bought a hot pizza.

DESCRIBING WORDS
Answer
2

hot

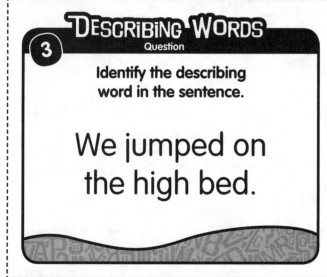

DESCRIBING WORDS
Question
3

Identify the describing word in the sentence.

We jumped on the high bed.

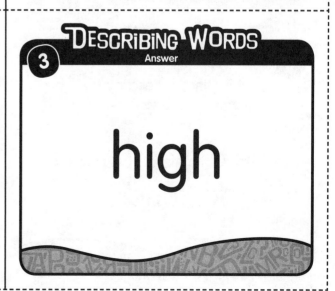

DESCRIBING WORDS
Answer
3

Instructions: Cut out each card along the dotted line. Then fold each card in half so the question is on one side and the answer is on the back. Glue or tape the cards together to keep the answers and questions on opposite sides.

DESCRIBING WORDS
Question

4

Identify the describing word in the sentence.

We went for a long walk.

DESCRIBING WORDS
Answer

4

long

DESCRIBING WORDS
Question

5

Identify the describing word in the sentence.

The tall building had lots of people.

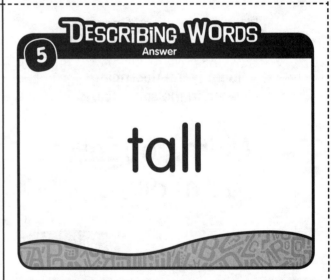

DESCRIBING WORDS
Answer

5

tall

DESCRIBING WORDS
Question

6

Identify the describing word in the sentence.

I ate a green apple for lunch.

DESCRIBING WORDS
Answer

6

green

Cooperative Learning & Grammar
Kagan Publishing • 1 (800) 933-2667 • www.KaganOnline.com

Instructions: Cut out each card along the dotted line. Then fold each card in half so the question is on one side and the answer is on the back. Glue or tape the cards together to keep the answers and questions on opposite sides.

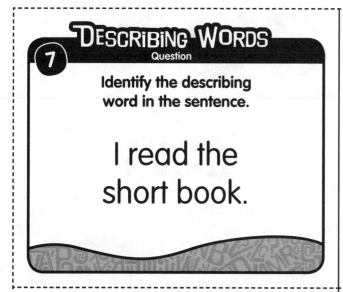

DESCRIBING WORDS
Question **7**

Identify the describing word in the sentence.

I read the short book.

DESCRIBING WORDS
Answer **7**

short

DESCRIBING WORDS
Question **8**

Identify the describing word in the sentence.

The dark clouds filled the sky.

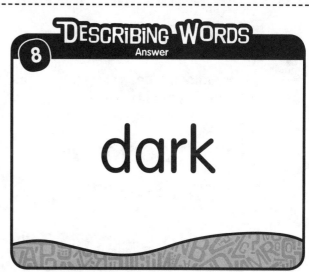

DESCRIBING WORDS
Answer **8**

dark

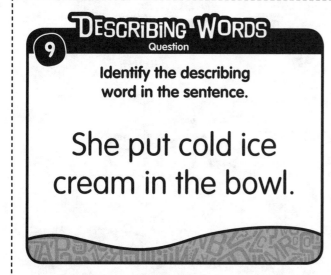

DESCRIBING WORDS
Question **9**

Identify the describing word in the sentence.

She put cold ice cream in the bowl.

DESCRIBING WORDS
Answer **9**

cold

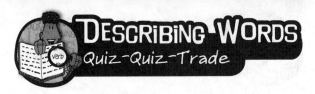

DESCRIBING WORDS
Quiz-Quiz-Trade

Instructions: Cut out each card along the dotted line. Then fold each card in half so the question is on one side and the answer is on the back. Glue or tape the cards together to keep the answers and questions on opposite sides.

DESCRIBING WORDS *Question*

10

Identify the describing word in the sentence.

The cold swimming pool had a diving board.

DESCRIBING WORDS *Answer*

10

cold

DESCRIBING WORDS *Question*

11

Identify the describing word in the sentence.

Don't spill the hot cup of water.

DESCRIBING WORDS *Answer*

11

hot

DESCRIBING WORDS *Question*

12

Identify the describing word in the sentence.

Have you seen my white sweater?

DESCRIBING WORDS *Answer*

12

white

Cooperative Learning & Grammar
Kagan Publishing • 1 (800) 933-2667 • www.KaganOnline.com

Instructions: Cut out each card along the dotted line. Then fold each card in half so the question is on one side and the answer is on the back. Glue or tape the cards together to keep the answers and questions on opposite sides.

DESCRIBING WORDS
Question
13

Identify the describing word in the sentence.

Please pass the sharp pencil.

DESCRIBING WORDS
Answer
13

sharp

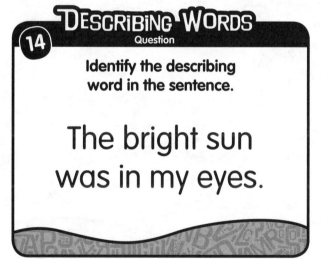

DESCRIBING WORDS
Question
14

Identify the describing word in the sentence.

The bright sun was in my eyes.

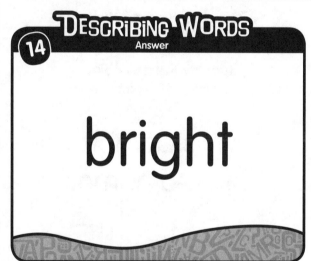

DESCRIBING WORDS
Answer
14

bright

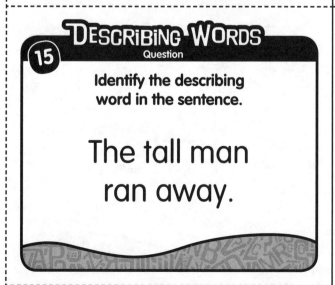

DESCRIBING WORDS
Question
15

Identify the describing word in the sentence.

The tall man ran away.

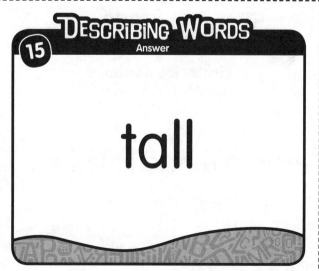

DESCRIBING WORDS
Answer
15

tall

DESCRIBING WORDS
Quiz-Quiz-Trade

Instructions: Cut out each card along the dotted line. Then fold each card in half so the question is on one side and the answer is on the back. Glue or tape the cards together to keep the answers and questions on opposite sides.

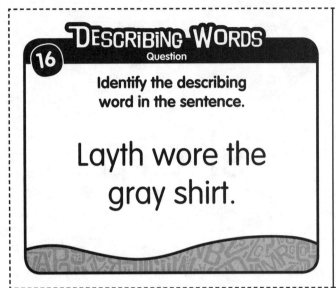

DESCRIBING WORDS
Question

16

Identify the describing word in the sentence.

Layth wore the gray shirt.

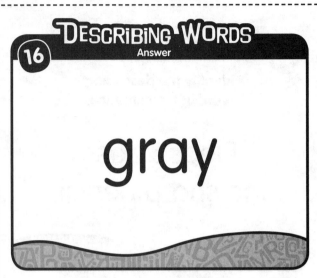

DESCRIBING WORDS
Answer

16

gray

DESCRIBING WORDS
Question

17

Identify the describing word in the sentence.

My sick mom stayed home.

DESCRIBING WORDS
Answer

17

sick

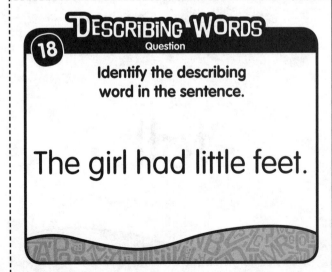

DESCRIBING WORDS
Question

18

Identify the describing word in the sentence.

The girl had little feet.

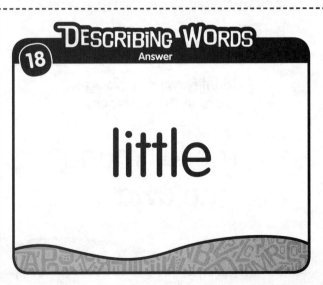

DESCRIBING WORDS
Answer

18

little

Cooperative Learning & Grammar
Kagan Publishing • 1 (800) 933-2667 • www.KaganOnline.com

DESCRIBING WORDS
Quiz-Quiz-Trade

Instructions: Cut out each card along the dotted line. Then fold each card in half so the question is on one side and the answer is on the back. Glue or tape the cards together to keep the answers and questions on opposite sides.

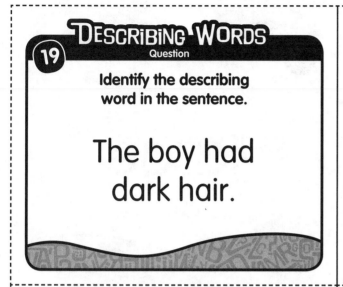

DESCRIBING WORDS
19 Question

Identify the describing word in the sentence.

The boy had dark hair.

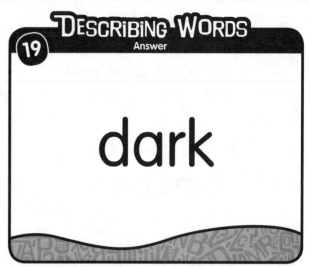

DESCRIBING WORDS
19 Answer

dark

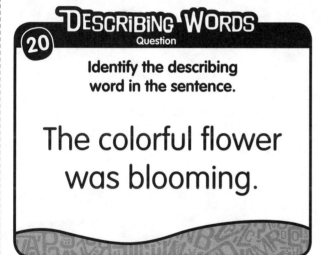

DESCRIBING WORDS
20 Question

Identify the describing word in the sentence.

The colorful flower was blooming.

DESCRIBING WORDS
20 Answer

colorful

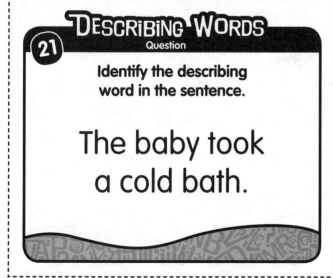

DESCRIBING WORDS
21 Question

Identify the describing word in the sentence.

The baby took a cold bath.

DESCRIBING WORDS
21 Answer

cold

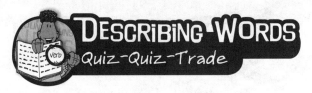

DESCRIBING WORDS
Quiz-Quiz-Trade

Instructions: Cut out each card along the dotted line. Then fold each card in half so the question is on one side and the answer is on the back. Glue or tape the cards together to keep the answers and questions on opposite sides.

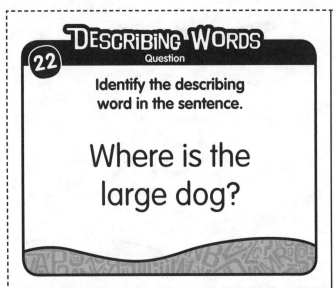

DESCRIBING WORDS
22 Question

Identify the describing word in the sentence.

Where is the large dog?

DESCRIBING WORDS
22 Answer

large

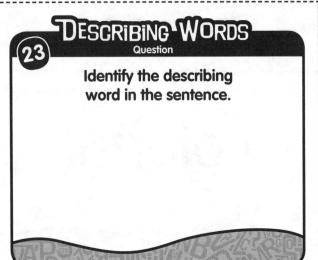

DESCRIBING WORDS
23 Question

Identify the describing word in the sentence.

DESCRIBING WORDS
23 Answer

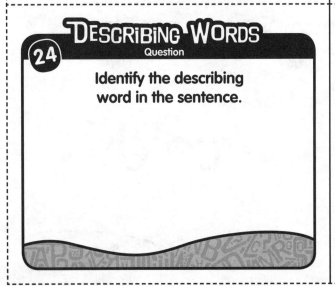

DESCRIBING WORDS
24 Question

Identify the describing word in the sentence.

DESCRIBING WORDS
24 Answer

Cooperative Learning & Grammar
Kagan Publishing • 1 (800) 933-2667 • www.KaganOnline.com

TYPES OF NOUNS
RallyCoach/Sage-N-Scribe

KEY IDEA

Nouns are people, places, or things. Below are examples of nouns in each category.

People		Places		Things	
doctor	actor	gym	school	tree	cowboy boot
teacher	child	dance studio	store	pencil	truck

Instructions: Write the words from the box in the category they belong. Take turns working with your partner to categorize each word using RallyCoach or Sage-N-Scribe.

PARTNER A	PARTNER B

Name _____   Name _____

| hospital   parent   computer | garage   baker   blanket |
| marble   farm   singer | train   park   author |

Places

_____

_____

Places

_____

_____

Things

_____

_____

Things

_____

_____

People

_____

_____

People

_____

_____

IDENTIFYING NOUNS
RallyCoach/Sage-N-Scribe

Instructions: Circle the noun to match the picture and then write it in the blank. Take turns working with your partner to solve the problems using RallyCoach or Sage-N-Scribe.

PARTNER A

Name _____

1

The teacher has a _____ on her desk.

a. student

b. lamp

c. book

2

The _____ floated high into the sky.

a. flower

b. birds

c. balloon

3

The young boy built a _____ out of blocks.

a. house

b. road

c. castle

PARTNER B

Name _____

1

The firefighter drove the _____ to the fire.

a. wagon

b. car

c. truck

2

The garden had many _____ growing.

a. weeds

b. flowers

c. trees

3

The _____ had a hole in the pocket.

a. jacket

b. hat

c. pant

Cooperative Learning & Grammar
Kagan Publishing • 1 (800) 933-2667 • www.KaganOnline.com

Instructions: Pair up and take turns identifying the noun. Write "person," "place," or "thing" in the box provided. Don't forget to get your partner's initials.

Word	Type of Noun	Initials
1 Pool		
2 Police Officer		
3 Computer		
4 Teacher		
5 Ball		
6 Park		
7 School		
8 Desk		
9 Bus Driver		

Instructions: Copy one set of cards for each team. Cut out each card along the dotted line. Give each team a set of cards to play Fan-N-Pick or Showdown.

NOUNS

1

Find two nouns in the sentence.

The house had one dog.

NOUNS

2

Find two nouns in the sentence.

The cat ran to the girl.

NOUNS

3

Find two nouns in the sentence.

The door shut in the wind.

NOUNS

4

Find two nouns in the sentence.

Lily's frog hopped away.

NOUNS

5

Find two nouns in the sentence.

The big computer fell on the floor.

NOUNS

6

Find two nouns in the sentence.

Mom made pizza.

Cooperative Learning & Grammar
Kagan Publishing • 1 (800) 933-2667 • www.KaganOnline.com

Instructions: Copy one set of cards for each team. Cut out each card along the dotted line. Give each team a set of cards to play Fan-N-Pick or Showdown.

NOUNS

7 Find two nouns in the sentence.

The baby crawled to the toy.

NOUNS

8 Find two nouns in the sentence.

The baseball hit the window.

NOUNS

9 Find two nouns in the sentence.

The phone rang in the kitchen.

NOUNS

10 Find two nouns in the sentence.

Tires roll down the street.

NOUNS

11 Find two nouns in the sentence.

The pond had two fish.

NOUNS

12 Find two nouns in the sentence.

Can Sally go to the park?

Instructions: Cut out each card along the dotted line. Then fold each card in half so the question is on one side and the answer is on the back. Glue or tape the cards together to keep the answers and questions on opposite sides.

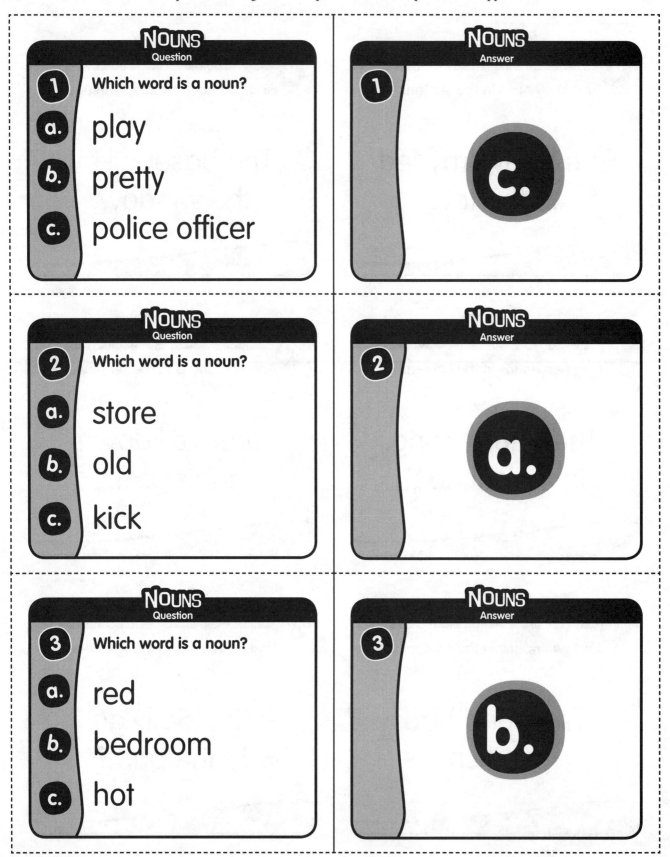

NOUNS Question

1 Which word is a noun?

a. play

b. pretty

c. police officer

NOUNS Answer

1 c.

NOUNS Question

2 Which word is a noun?

a. store

b. old

c. kick

NOUNS Answer

2 a.

NOUNS Question

3 Which word is a noun?

a. red

b. bedroom

c. hot

NOUNS Answer

3 b.

Cooperative Learning & Grammar
Kagan Publishing • 1 (800) 933-2667 • www.KaganOnline.com

NOUNS
Quiz-Quiz-Trade

Instructions: Cut out each card along the dotted line. Then fold each card in half so the question is on one side and the answer is on the back. Glue or tape the cards together to keep the answers and questions on opposite sides.

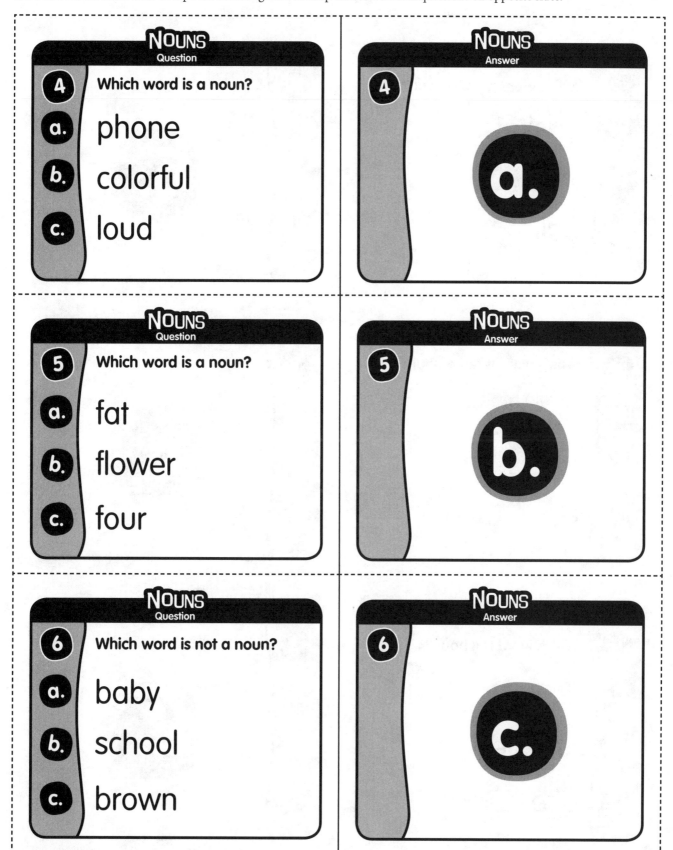

NOUNS
Question

4. Which word is a noun?
a. phone
b. colorful
c. loud

NOUNS
Answer

4. a.

NOUNS
Question

5. Which word is a noun?
a. fat
b. flower
c. four

NOUNS
Answer

5. b.

NOUNS
Question

6. Which word is not a noun?
a. baby
b. school
c. brown

NOUNS
Answer

6. c.

Instructions: Cut out each card along the dotted line. Then fold each card in half so the question is on one side and the answer is on the back. Glue or tape the cards together to keep the answers and questions on opposite sides.

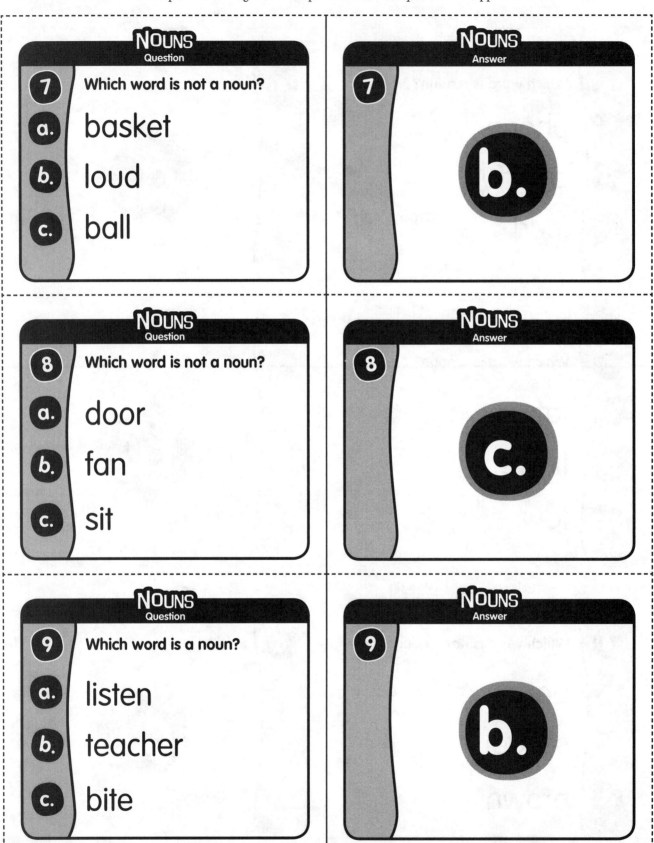

NOUNS
Question

7 Which word is not a noun?

a. basket

b. loud

c. ball

NOUNS
Answer

7

b.

NOUNS
Question

8 Which word is not a noun?

a. door

b. fan

c. sit

NOUNS
Answer

8

c.

NOUNS
Question

9 Which word is a noun?

a. listen

b. teacher

c. bite

NOUNS
Answer

9

b.

Cooperative Learning & Grammar
Kagan Publishing • 1 (800) 933-2667 • www.KaganOnline.com

Instructions: Cut out each card along the dotted line. Then fold each card in half so the question is on one side and the answer is on the back. Glue or tape the cards together to keep the answers and questions on opposite sides.

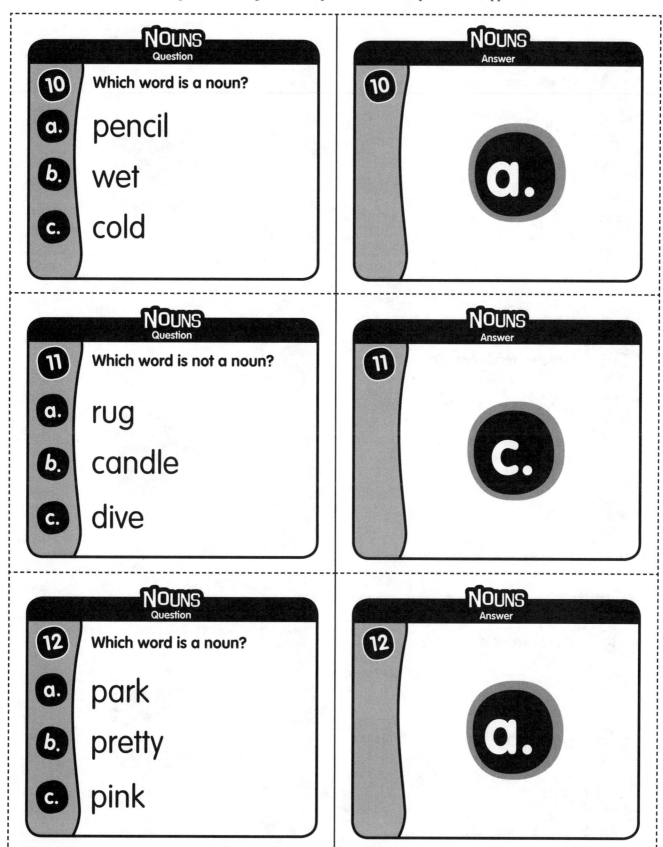

NOUNS
Question

10 Which word is a noun?

a. pencil

b. wet

c. cold

NOUNS
Answer

10 a.

NOUNS
Question

11 Which word is not a noun?

a. rug

b. candle

c. dive

NOUNS
Answer

11 c.

NOUNS
Question

12 Which word is a noun?

a. park

b. pretty

c. pink

NOUNS
Answer

12 a.

NOUNS
Quiz-Quiz-Trade

Instructions: Cut out each card along the dotted line. Then fold each card in half so the question is on one side and the answer is on the back. Glue or tape the cards together to keep the answers and questions on opposite sides.

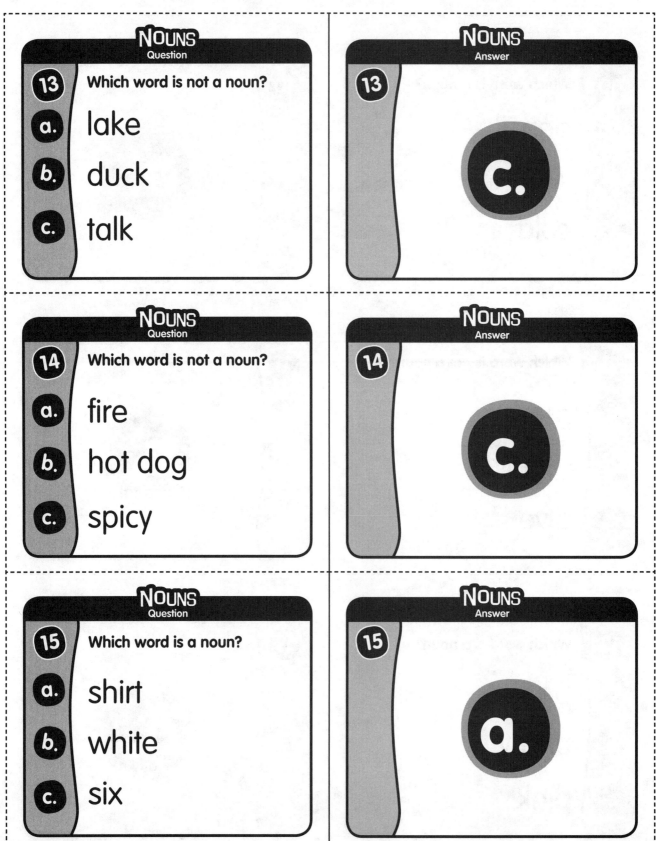

NOUNS Question

13 Which word is not a noun?

a. lake

b. duck

c. talk

NOUNS Answer

13 c.

NOUNS Question

14 Which word is not a noun?

a. fire

b. hot dog

c. spicy

NOUNS Answer

14 c.

NOUNS Question

15 Which word is a noun?

a. shirt

b. white

c. six

NOUNS Answer

15 a.

Cooperative Learning & Grammar
Kagan Publishing • 1 (800) 933-2667 • www.KaganOnline.com

Instructions: Cut out each card along the dotted line. Then fold each card in half so the question is on one side and the answer is on the back. Glue or tape the cards together to keep the answers and questions on opposite sides.

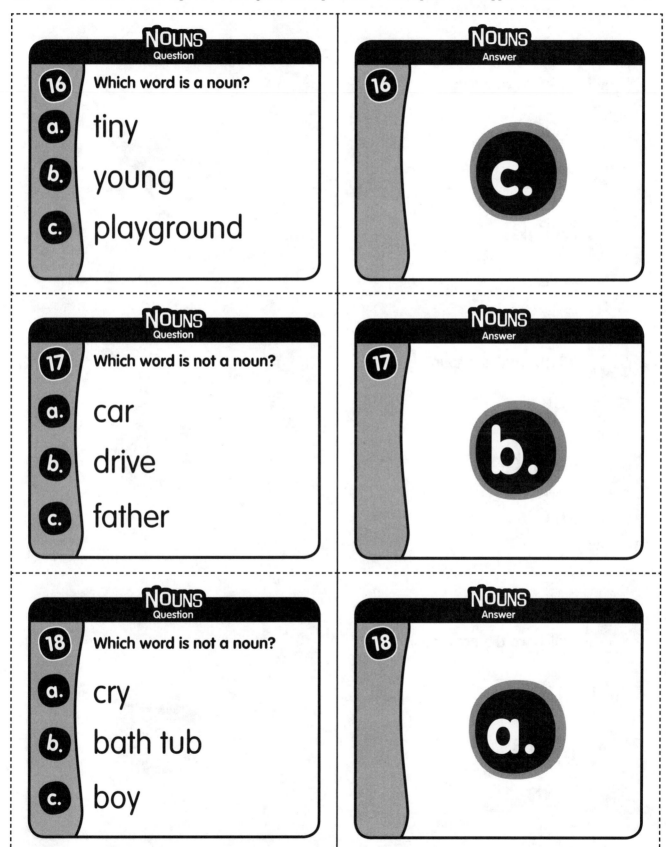

NOUNS
Question

16 Which word is a noun?

a. tiny

b. young

c. playground

NOUNS
Answer

16

c.

NOUNS
Question

17 Which word is not a noun?

a. car

b. drive

c. father

NOUNS
Answer

17

b.

NOUNS
Question

18 Which word is not a noun?

a. cry

b. bath tub

c. boy

NOUNS
Answer

18

a.

NOUNS
Quiz-Quiz-Trade

Instructions: Cut out each card along the dotted line. Then fold each card in half so the question is on one side and the answer is on the back. Glue or tape the cards together to keep the answers and questions on opposite sides.

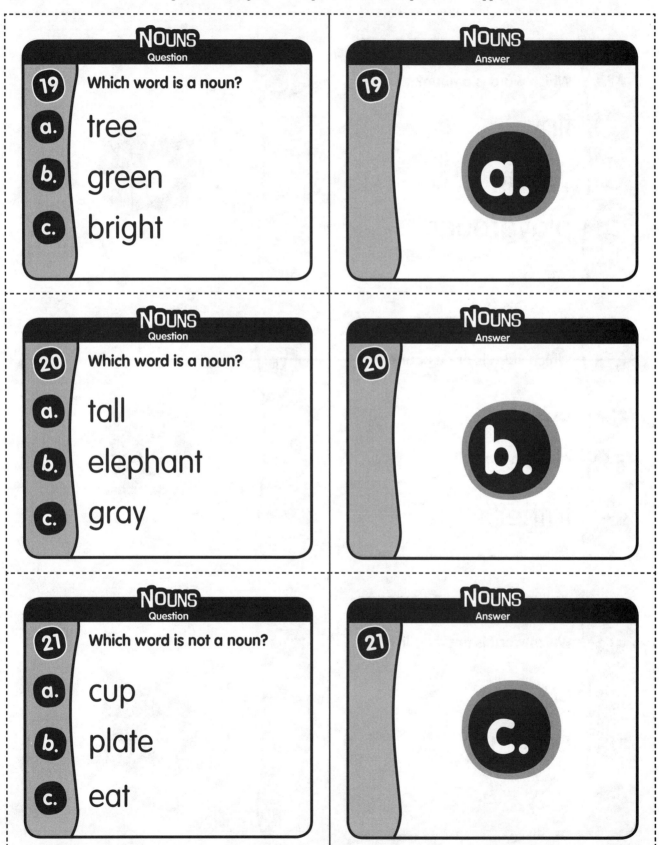

NOUNS
Question

19 Which word is a noun?

a. tree

b. green

c. bright

NOUNS
Answer

19

a.

NOUNS
Question

20 Which word is a noun?

a. tall

b. elephant

c. gray

NOUNS
Answer

20

b.

NOUNS
Question

21 Which word is not a noun?

a. cup

b. plate

c. eat

NOUNS
Answer

21

c.

Cooperative Learning & Grammar
Kagan Publishing • 1 (800) 933-2667 • www.KaganOnline.com

PLURAL NOUNS
RallyCoach/Sage-N-Scribe

KEY IDEA

Plural nouns mean more than one. Add –s to nouns to show more than one. Add –es to nouns that end –sh, -s, -x, or –ch

–s Examples: dog—dogs; house—houses; car—cars

–es Examples: brush—brushes; dress—dresses; ax—axes; church—churches

Instructions: Make each noun plural by adding –s or –es to the end of the word. Write the new word on the line. Take turns working with your partner to solve the problems using RallyCoach or Sage-N-Scribe.

PARTNER A	PARTNER B
Name _____	Name _____
1 Bird _____	**1** Tree _____
2 Shirt _____	**2** Couch _____
3 Toy _____	**3** Phone _____
4 Bush _____	**4** Monkey _____
5 Sandwich _____	**5** Fox _____

Plural Nouns
Find Someone Who

Name _____

Instructions: Pair up and take turns circling the word that matches the picture. Don't forget to get your partner's initials.

1

pencil   pencils

Initials

2

cat   cats

Initials

3

drum   drums

Initials

4

duck   ducks

Initials

5

boys   boy

Initials

6

shirt   shirts

Initials

Cooperative Learning & Grammar
Kagan Publishing • 1 (800) 933-2667 • www.KaganOnline.com

Instructions: Take turns working with your partner to underline the nouns and to circle the action word in each sentence. The number of nouns is stated at the end of the sentence. Use RallyCoach or Sage-N-Scribe to solve the problems.

	PARTNER A		PARTNER B
Name		Name	
1	Leonard wrote his name on the paper. (3)	**1**	The puppets danced in the show. (2)
2	The water runs quickly down the stream. (2)	**2**	A monkey climbed the tree. (2)
3	The alarm clock chirps loudly in the room. (2)	**3**	The boat soared through the lake and streams. (3)
4	A rainbow stretches across the sky. (2)	**4**	A hamster spins his wheel in the large cage. (3)
5	The movie plays on the television and the computer. (3)	**5**	The teacher reads a book to the students. (3)
6	Mom packed soda, sandwiches, and carrots for the picnic. (5)	**6**	A skateboard rolls down the empty street. (2)

Instructions: Take turns working with your partner to circle the action word and put an "X" over the describing word in each sentence. The naming words are underlined in the sentences below. Use RallyCoach or Sage-N-Scribe to solve the problems.

PARTNER A

Name _____

1. Larry kicked the red ball.

2. The dirty shirt needs to be washed.

3. The old dinosaur growled loudly.

4. Michele planted yellow and pink flowers in her garden.

5. The noisy crowd cheered loudly for the winning team.

6. Millie swam in the refreshing lake.

7. The train sped down the long tracks.

8. The baby cries for a warm bottle.

9. James walked the black dog.

10. The green grass grows in the light.

PARTNER B

Name _____

1. The warm pancakes filled my belly.

2. My red shoes fit my feet like a sock.

3. The purple balloon floated in the sky.

4. Dee baked fresh rolls and yummy cupcakes.

5. The grand piano made beautiful music from the stage.

6. Brett read on the comfy sofa.

7. The curious monkey climbed a tree.

8. Fredrick told me a silly story.

9. The loud thunder shook the house.

10. The large clock chimed in the kitchen.

Cooperative Learning & Grammar
Kagan Publishing • 1 (800) 933-2667 • www.KaganOnline.com

Instructions: Pair up and take turns placing a word from the Word Bank in the correct category below. Don't forget to get your partner's initials.

WORD BANK

pretty	jump	girl	man	old
big	teacher	run	kick	boy
computer	ugly	fat	chew	swim

Noun	Describing Word	Action Word
_____	_____	_____
Initials	Initials	Initials
_____	_____	_____
Initials	Initials	Initials
_____	_____	_____
Initials	Initials	Initials
_____	_____	_____
Initials	Initials	Initials
_____	_____	_____
Initials	Initials	Initials

Instructions: Pair up and take turns writing the correct noun and action word from the Word Bank that best describe the picture. Don't forget to get your partner's initials.

WORD BANK

cat	man	draw	girl	frog	eat
dog	sleep	catch	boy	jump	drive

1

_____
Noun

_____
Action

Initials
_____

2

_____
Noun

_____
Action

Initials
_____

3

_____
Noun

_____
Action

Initials
_____

4

_____
Noun

_____
Action

Initials
_____

5

_____
Noun

_____
Action

Initials
_____

6

_____
Noun

_____
Action

Initials
_____

Cooperative Learning & Grammar
Kagan Publishing • 1 (800) 933-2667 • www.KaganOnline.com

PRONOUNS
RallyCoach/Sage-N-Scribe

Pronouns take the place of a noun. Below are a few examples.

Examples: <u>James</u> is walking the dog. <u>He</u> is walking the dog.
<u>The girls</u> are singing a song. <u>They</u> are singing a song.

Pronoun List: He, She, It, They, Them, His, Hers, I , Us, We

Instructions: Replace the underlined noun with a pronoun. Write the pronoun on the line. Take turns working with your partner to solve the problems using RallyCoach or Sage-N-Scribe.

PARTNER A

Name _____

1 <u>Billy</u> kicked the ball to James.
_____
_____
_____

2 There is a hole in the <u>shirt</u>.
_____
_____
_____

3 <u>Penny and I</u> are going to the school.
_____
_____
_____

4 <u>The horse</u> ran down in the field.
_____
_____
_____

5 Give the pencil to <u>Julie and Kim</u>.
_____
_____
_____

PARTNER B

Name _____

1 <u>The piano</u> has broken keys.
_____
_____
_____

2 <u>The donkey</u> is eating the hay.
_____
_____
_____

3 <u>Caleb and Colton</u> are brothers.
_____
_____
_____

4 <u>Melissa</u> is my best friend.
_____
_____
_____

5 Answer <u>the phone</u>.
_____
_____
_____

PRONOUNS
Find Someone Who

Instructions: Pair up and take turns circling the pronoun that best describes the picture. Don't forget to get your partner's initials.

1
a. she
b. him
c. they

Initials

2
a. him
b. it
c. they

Initials

3
a. they
b. them
c. he

Initials

4
a. they
b. we
c. he

Initials

5
a. it
b. them
c. she

Initials

6
a. I
b. we
c. they

Initials

Cooperative Learning & Grammar
Kagan Publishing • 1 (800) 933-2667 • www.KaganOnline.com

PRONOUNS
Find Someone Who

Instructions: Pair up and take turns circling the pronoun in the sentence. Don't forget to get your partner's initials.

1 How long will she be gone? *Initials*

2 He forgot the homework. *Initials*

3 Did they enjoy the movie? *Initials*

4 When will we get to the park? *Initials*

5 John lost his mittens. *Initials*

6 Did her mom pick up the pizza? *Initials*

7 He ran down the street. *Initials*

8 How long did it take them? *Initials*

9 Did Shelly talk to him yesterday? *Initials*

PRONOUNS
Fan-N-Pick/Showdown

Instructions: Copy one set of cards for each team. Cut out each card along the dotted line. Give each team a set of cards to play Fan-N-Pick or Showdown.

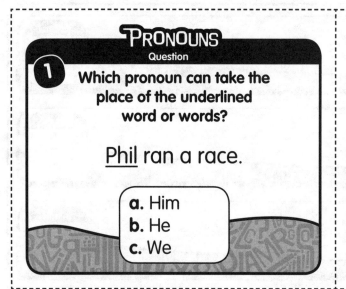

PRONOUNS
Question

1 Which pronoun can take the place of the underlined word or words?

<u>Phil</u> ran a race.

a. Him
b. He
c. We

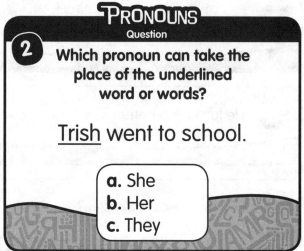

PRONOUNS
Question

2 Which pronoun can take the place of the underlined word or words?

<u>Trish</u> went to school.

a. She
b. Her
c. They

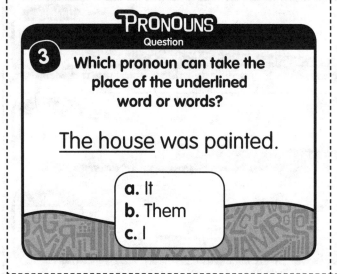

PRONOUNS
Question

3 Which pronoun can take the place of the underlined word or words?

<u>The house</u> was painted.

a. It
b. Them
c. I

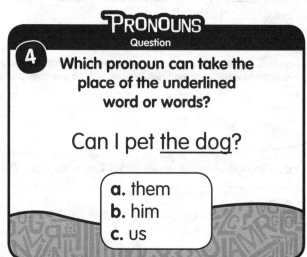

PRONOUNS
Question

4 Which pronoun can take the place of the underlined word or words?

Can I pet <u>the dog</u>?

a. them
b. him
c. us

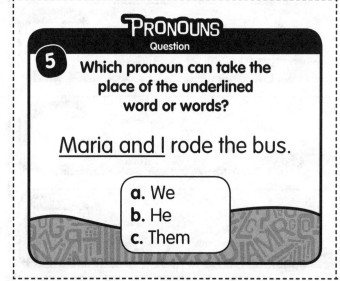

PRONOUNS
Question

5 Which pronoun can take the place of the underlined word or words?

<u>Maria and I</u> rode the bus.

a. We
b. He
c. Them

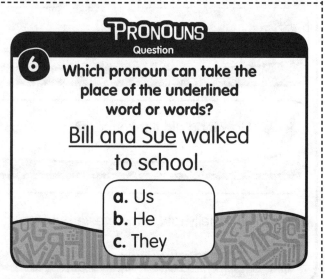

PRONOUNS
Question

6 Which pronoun can take the place of the underlined word or words?

<u>Bill and Sue</u> walked to school.

a. Us
b. He
c. They

Cooperative Learning & Grammar
Kagan Publishing • 1 (800) 933-2667 • www.KaganOnline.com

PRONOUNS
Fan-N-Pick/Showdown

Instructions: Copy one set of cards for each team. Cut out each card along the dotted line. Give each team a set of cards to play Fan-N-Pick or Showdown.

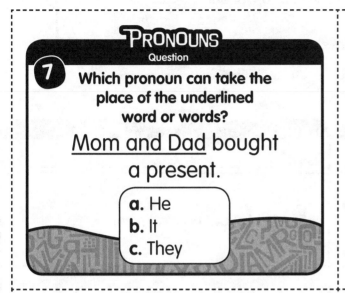

PRONOUNS
Question

7 Which pronoun can take the place of the underlined word or words?

<u>Mom and Dad</u> bought a present.

a. He
b. It
c. They

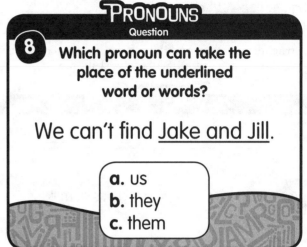

PRONOUNS
Question

8 Which pronoun can take the place of the underlined word or words?

We can't find <u>Jake and Jill</u>.

a. us
b. they
c. them

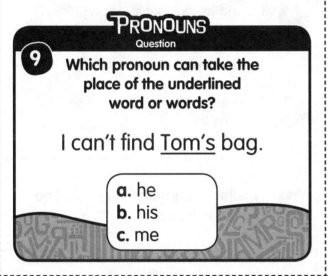

PRONOUNS
Question

9 Which pronoun can take the place of the underlined word or words?

I can't find <u>Tom's</u> bag.

a. he
b. his
c. me

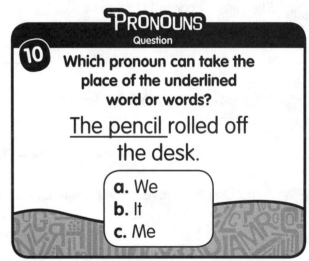

PRONOUNS
Question

10 Which pronoun can take the place of the underlined word or words?

<u>The pencil</u> rolled off the desk.

a. We
b. It
c. Me

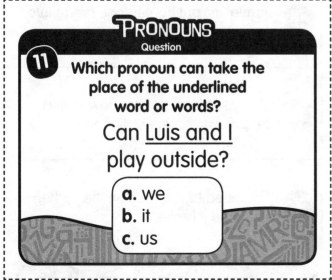

PRONOUNS
Question

11 Which pronoun can take the place of the underlined word or words?

Can <u>Luis and I</u> play outside?

a. we
b. it
c. us

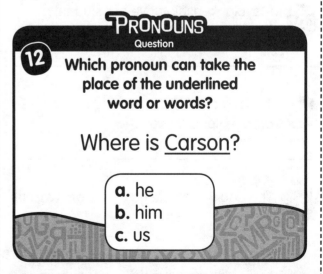

PRONOUNS
Question

12 Which pronoun can take the place of the underlined word or words?

Where is <u>Carson</u>?

a. he
b. him
c. us

A OR AN?
RallyCoach/Sage-N-Scribe

KEY IDEA The words "a" and "an" help point out a person, place or thing. Use "a" before a word that begins with a consonant. Use "an" before a word that begins with a vowel.

Examples: Laura read <u>a</u> story. It was about <u>an</u> octopus.

Instructions: Take turns working with your partner to circle either "a" or "an" to correctly complete each sentence. Use RallyCoach or Sage-N-Scribe to solve the problem.

PARTNER A	PARTNER B
Name _____	Name _____
1 George wants **(a, an)** glass of milk.	**1** **(A, An)** owl hoots at night.
2 The remote control car ran up **(a, an)** ramp.	**2** I found **(a, an)** lost key to a hidden treasure.
3 Michael is excited to fly on **(a, an)** airplane.	**3** The playground has **(a, an)** set of safety rules.
4 Tracy asked to have **(a, an)** apple for her lunch box.	**4** I might need **(a, an)** umbrella if I go outside in the rain.
5 Ms. Blankenship gave her students **(a, an)** book to read.	**5** Jamie just put homemade bread into **(a, an)** oven to bake.
6 Juli asked her sister to bring her **(a, an)** orange soda at work.	**6** Can you please tell me how to find **(a, an)** word in the dictionary?
7 The dog wanted to go for **(a, an)** walk in the park.	**7** I dropped **(a, an)** dish on the kitchen floor and it broke.

Cooperative Learning & Grammar
Kagan Publishing • 1 (800) 933-2667 • www.KaganOnline.com

Instructions: Pair up and take turns writing either "a" or "an" in the blank to correctly complete each sentence below. Don't forget to get your partner's initials.

1

I would like _____
(a, an)
apple for lunch.

Initials

2

My mom bought us

_____ snack.
(a, an)

Initials

3

I can play _____
(a, an)
piano.

Initials

4

I wore _____
(a, an)
orange shirt to

school.

Initials

5

The dog ran away

with _____ stick.
(a, an)

Initials

6

Some kids bring

_____ lunch to
(a, an)
school.

Initials

7 We will have

to take _____
(a, an)
umbrella with us

to the movies.

Initials

8

The monkey was

eating _____
(a, an)
banana.

Initials

9

The playground was

wet from _____
(a, an)
rainstorm.

Initials

ARTICLES
Fan-N-Pick/Showdown

Instructions: Copy one set of cards for each team. Cut out each card along the dotted line. Give each team a set of cards to play Fan-N-Pick or Showdown.

ARTICLES

1 Choose the article to complete the sentence below.

Mom found _____ (a, an) gray sweater.

ARTICLES

2 Choose the article to complete the sentence below.

Betty lost _____ (a, an) orange sock.

ARTICLES

3 Choose the article to complete the sentence below.

Why can you not get _____ (a, an) dog?

ARTICLES

4 Choose the article to complete the sentence below.

We can play _____ (a, an) piano.

ARTICLES

5 Choose the article to complete the sentence below.

Fernando was _____ (a, an) elephant for Halloween.

ARTICLES

6 Choose the article to complete the sentence below.

Who would like _____ (a, an) ice cream cone?

Cooperative Learning & Grammar
Kagan Publishing • 1 (800) 933-2667 • www.KaganOnline.com

Instructions: Copy one set of cards for each team. Cut out each card along the dotted line. Give each team a set of cards to play Fan-N-Pick or Showdown.

ARTICLES

7

Choose the article to complete the sentence below.

Maria enjoyed _____
(a, an)
cupcake for dessert.

ARTICLES

8

Choose the article to complete the sentence below.

Mrs. Thompson gave us
_____ extra recess.
(a, an)

ARTICLES

9

Choose the article to complete the sentence below.

Would you like _____ bird
(a, an)
for your birthday?

ARTICLES

10

Choose the article to complete the sentence below.

I ate _____ apple for lunch.
(a, an)

ARTICLES

11

Choose the article to complete the sentence below.

We saw _____ duck
(a, an)
at the park.

ARTICLES

12

Choose the article to complete the sentence below.

Susie's mom bought her
_____ cat.
(a, an)

COMPOUND WORDS
RallyCoach/Sage-N-Scribe

KEY IDEA Compound words are when two words are put together to form a new word.

Example: sun + shine = sunshine

Instructions: Make each word below a compound word by adding a word from the Word Bank. Take turns working with your partner to solve the problems using RallyCoach or Sage-N-Scribe.

PARTNER A	PARTNER B
Name _____	**Name** _____

Word Bank

PARTNER A	PARTNER B
hot bow sand cake walk	boy corn foot pan sail

1 _____castle

1 _____boat

2 cup_____

2 pop_____

3 _____dog

3 _____ball

4 side_____

4 _____cake

5 hair_____

5 cow_____

Cooperative Learning & Grammar
Kagan Publishing • 1 (800) 933-2667 • www.KaganOnline.com

Instructions: Pair up and take turns circling the word that makes the underlined word into a compound word. Don't forget to get your partner's initials.

1 Which word would you add to <u>mail</u> to make it a compound word?

a. shoe
b. box
c. key

Initials

2 Which word would you add to <u>sun</u> to make it a compound word?

a. box
b. table
c. shine

Initials

3 Which word would you add to <u>base</u> to make it a compound word?

a. glove
b. ball
c. door

Initials

4 Which word would you add to <u>every</u> to make it a compound word?

a. thing
b. book
c. desk

Initials

5 Which word would you add to <u>rain</u> to make it a compound word?

a. shine
b. bow
c. desk

Initials

6 Which word would you add to <u>head</u> to make it a compound word?

a. light
b. sky
c. boy

Initials

7 Which word would you add to <u>door</u> to make it a compound word?

a. key
b. light
c. knob

Initials

8 Which word would you add to <u>tooth</u> to make it a compound word?

a. brush
b. hair
c. key

Initials

9 Which word would you add to <u>birth</u> to make it a compound word?

a. month
b. boy
c. day

Initials

Instructions: Cut out the cards on the dotted line. Give one card to each student. Distribute cards in sequence so for every student with a word card, there is a student with a matching word card to form a compound word.

COMPOUND WORDS

What word can you add to the word below to make a compound word?

sun_____

COMPOUND WORDS

What word can you add to the word below to make a compound word?

_____flower

COMPOUND WORDS

What word can you add to the word below to make a compound word?

base_____

COMPOUND WORDS

What word can you add to the word below to make a compound word?

_____ball

COMPOUND WORDS

What word can you add to the word below to make a compound word?

rain_____

COMPOUND WORDS

What word can you add to the word below to make a compound word?

_____bow

Cooperative Learning & Grammar
Kagan Publishing • 1 (800) 933-2667 • www.KaganOnline.com

Instructions: Cut out the cards on the dotted line. Give one card to each student. Distribute cards in sequence so for every student with a word card, there is a student with a matching word card to form a compound word.

COMPOUND WORDS

What word can you add to the word below to make a compound word?

birth_____

COMPOUND WORDS

What word can you add to the word below to make a compound word?

_____day

COMPOUND WORDS

What word can you add to the word below to make a compound word?

cow_____

COMPOUND WORDS

What word can you add to the word below to make a compound word?

_____boy

COMPOUND WORDS

What word can you add to the word below to make a compound word?

air_____

COMPOUND WORDS

What word can you add to the word below to make a compound word?

_____plane

COMPOUND WORDS
Mix-N-Match

Instructions: Cut out the cards on the dotted line. Give one card to each student. Distribute cards in sequence so for every student with a word card, there is a student with a matching word card to form a compound word.

COMPOUND WORDS

What word can you add to the word below to make a compound word?

back_____

COMPOUND WORDS

What word can you add to the word below to make a compound word?

_____yard

COMPOUND WORDS

What word can you add to the word below to make a compound word?

cup_____

COMPOUND WORDS

What word can you add to the word below to make a compound word?

_____cake

COMPOUND WORDS

What word can you add to the word below to make a compound word?

fire_____

COMPOUND WORDS

What word can you add to the word below to make a compound word?

_____place

Cooperative Learning & Grammar
Kagan Publishing • 1 (800) 933-2667 • www.KaganOnline.com

Instructions: Cut out the cards on the dotted line. Give one card to each student. Distribute cards in sequence so for every student with a word card, there is a student with a matching word card to form a compound word.

COMPOUND WORDS

What word can you add to the word below to make a compound word?

pop_____

COMPOUND WORDS

What word can you add to the word below to make a compound word?

_____corn

COMPOUND WORDS

What word can you add to the word below to make a compound word?

mail_____

COMPOUND WORDS

What word can you add to the word below to make a compound word?

_____box

COMPOUND WORDS

What word can you add to the word below to make a compound word?

play_____

COMPOUND WORDS

What word can you add to the word below to make a compound word?

_____ground

Instructions: Cut out the cards on the dotted line. Give one card to each student. Distribute cards in sequence so for every student with a word card, there is a student with a matching word card to form a compound word.

COMPOUND WORDS

What word can you add to the word below to make a compound word?

pea_____

COMPOUND WORDS

What word can you add to the word below to make a compound word?

_____nut

COMPOUND WORDS

What word can you add to the word below to make a compound word?

pan_____

COMPOUND WORDS

What word can you add to the word below to make a compound word?

_____cake

COMPOUND WORDS

What word can you add to the word below to make a compound word?

tooth_____

COMPOUND WORDS

What word can you add to the word below to make a compound word?

_____brush

COMPOUND WORDS
Mix-N-Match

Instructions: Cut out the cards on the dotted line. Give one card to each student. Distribute cards in sequence so for every student with a word card, there is a student with a matching word card to form a compound word.

COMPOUND WORDS
What word can you add to the word below to make a compound word?

after_____

COMPOUND WORDS
What word can you add to the word below to make a compound word?

_____noon

COMPOUND WORDS
What word can you add to the word below to make a compound word?

butter_____

COMPOUND WORDS
What word can you add to the word below to make a compound word?

_____fly

COMPOUND WORDS
What word can you add to the word below to make a compound word?

snow_____

COMPOUND WORDS
What word can you add to the word below to make a compound word?

_____man

KEY IDEA

A contraction is a short way of writing two words. In a contraction, you use an apostrophe (') to show when a letter or letters have been left out.

Example: I have = I've

Instructions: Write the contraction of the words on the line. Take turns working with your partner to solve the problems using RallyCoach or Sage-N-Scribe.

PARTNER A	PARTNER B
Name _____	Name _____
1 do not = _____	**1** I will = _____
2 I am = _____	**2** have not = _____
3 they are = _____	**3** we are = _____
4 it is = _____	**4** she is = _____
5 he is = _____	**5** he will = _____

Cooperative Learning & Grammar
Kagan Publishing • 1 (800) 933-2667 • www.KaganOnline.com

CONTRACTIONS
RallyCoach/Sage-N-Scribe

Instructions: Take turns working with your partner to circle the correct contraction to complete each sentence. Use RallyCoach or Sage-N-Scribe to solve the problem.

PARTNER A

Name _____

1 I **(don't/isn't)** need to do my homework tonight.

2 Meghan decided she **(haven't/doesn't)** have enough socks.

3 My mom **(hadn't/won't)** sign my reading log until I read my book.

4 Tommy **(I'm/can't)** play outside until he cleans his room.

5 I hope **(she'll/it's)** invite me to her birthday party.

6 Please **(won't/don't)** feed the bears at the zoo.

7 Mrs. Matzat **(didn't/don't)** read a new book in the library today.

8 Mr. Dawson **(isn't/won't)** tell us about the surprise.

PARTNER B

Name _____

1 The baby **(isn't/won't)** stop crying unless he is held.

2 I hope it **(won't/isn't)** too cold to go outside for recess.

3 **(I'm/They'll)** going to go swimming at my grandparents' house.

4 Clint and Kevin **(hasn't/haven't)** been to see a movie all summer.

5 **(We're/You'll)** playing football in the park at sunset.

6 Cami told her brother that she **(aren't/isn't)** coming to dinner.

7 Elmo **(can't/doesn't)** want to go to the store without his mom.

8 The mailman **(can't/I'm)** bring me my mail in the snowstorm.

Instructions: Pair up and take turns circling the correct contraction for the underlined words below. Don't forget to get your partner's initials.

1 Which contraction is made from the words <u>do</u> <u>not</u>?

ⓐ don't

ⓑ do'not

ⓒ do'nt

Initials

2 Which contraction is made from the words <u>I would</u>?

ⓐ I'wld

ⓑ Id'e

ⓒ I'd

Initials

3 Which contraction is made from the words <u>could</u> <u>not</u>?

ⓐ cldn't

ⓑ couldno't

ⓒ couldn't

Initials

4 Which contraction is written correctly?

ⓐ haveno't

ⓑ shouldn't

ⓒ shel'l

Initials

5 Which contraction is written correctly?

ⓐ can't

ⓑ ca'nt

ⓒ cant'

Initials

6 Which contraction is written correctly?

ⓐ that'is

ⓑ tha'ts

ⓒ that's

Initials

7 Which contraction is made from the words <u>she</u> <u>will</u>?

ⓐ she'l

ⓑ she'll

ⓒ she'will

Initials

8 Which contraction is made from the words <u>he</u> <u>would</u>?

ⓐ hewl'd

ⓑ he'wld

ⓒ he'd

Initials

9 Which contraction is made from the words <u>you</u> <u>are</u>?

ⓐ you're

ⓑ youre'

ⓒ your'e

Initials

Cooperative Learning & Grammar
Kagan Publishing • 1 (800) 933-2667 • www.KaganOnline.com

CONTRACTIONS
Fan-N-Pick/Showdown

Instructions: Copy one set of cards for each team. Cut out each card along the dotted line. Give each team a set of cards to play Fan-N-Pick or Showdown.

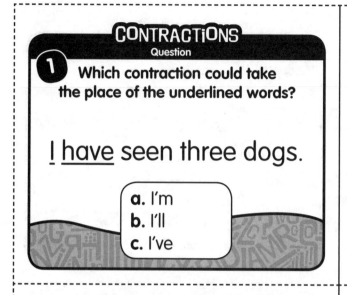

CONTRACTiONS
Question

1 Which contraction could take the place of the underlined words?

<u>I</u> <u>have</u> seen three dogs.

a. I'm
b. I'll
c. I've

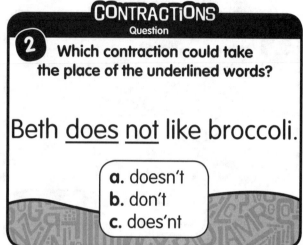

CONTRACTiONS
Question

2 Which contraction could take the place of the underlined words?

Beth <u>does</u> <u>not</u> like broccoli.

a. doesn't
b. don't
c. does'nt

CONTRACTiONS
Question

3 Which contraction could take the place of the underlined words?

Mom <u>did</u> <u>not</u> pack my lunch today.

a. don't
b. didn't
c. can't

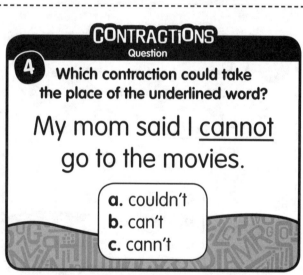

CONTRACTiONS
Question

4 Which contraction could take the place of the underlined word?

My mom said I <u>cannot</u> go to the movies.

a. couldn't
b. can't
c. cann't

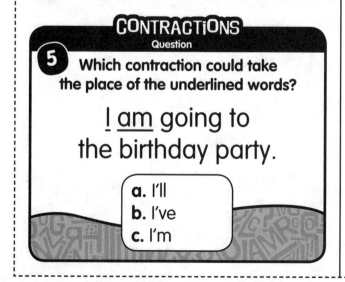

CONTRACTiONS
Question

5 Which contraction could take the place of the underlined words?

<u>I</u> <u>am</u> going to the birthday party.

a. I'll
b. I've
c. I'm

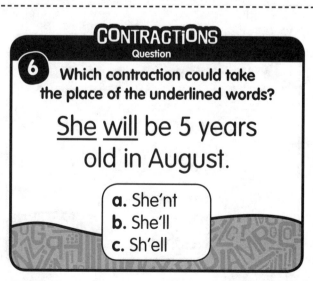

CONTRACTiONS
Question

6 Which contraction could take the place of the underlined words?

<u>She</u> <u>will</u> be 5 years old in August.

a. She'nt
b. She'll
c. Sh'ell

CONTRACTiONS
Fan-N-Pick/Showdown

Instructions: Copy one set of cards for each team. Cut out each card along the dotted line. Give each team a set of cards to play Fan-N-Pick or Showdown.

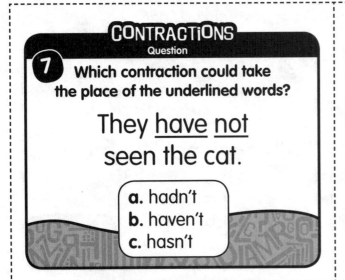

CONTRACTiONS
Question

7 Which contraction could take the place of the underlined words?

They <u>have</u> <u>not</u> seen the cat.

a. hadn't
b. haven't
c. hasn't

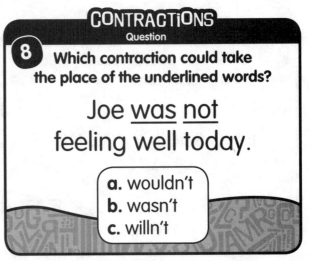

CONTRACTiONS
Question

8 Which contraction could take the place of the underlined words?

Joe <u>was</u> <u>not</u> feeling well today.

a. wouldn't
b. wasn't
c. willn't

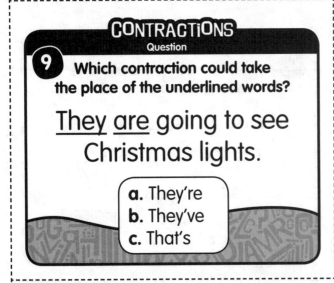

CONTRACTiONS
Question

9 Which contraction could take the place of the underlined words?

<u>They</u> <u>are</u> going to see Christmas lights.

a. They're
b. They've
c. That's

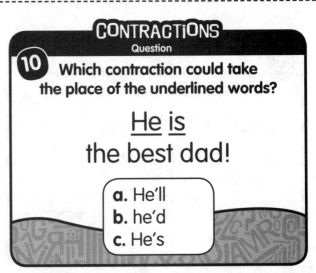

CONTRACTiONS
Question

10 Which contraction could take the place of the underlined words?

<u>He</u> <u>is</u> the best dad!

a. He'll
b. he'd
c. He's

CONTRACTiONS
Question

11 Which contraction could take the place of the underlined words?

How do you know <u>they</u> <u>will</u> be there?

a. they're
b. they'll
c. that's

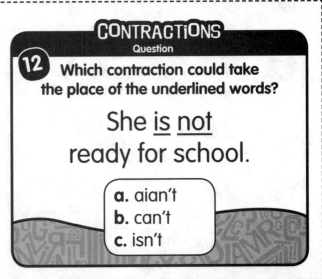

CONTRACTiONS
Question

12 Which contraction could take the place of the underlined words?

She <u>is</u> <u>not</u> ready for school.

a. aian't
b. can't
c. isn't

Cooperative Learning & Grammar
Kagan Publishing • 1 (800) 933-2667 • www.KaganOnline.com

CONTRACTiONS
Mix-N-Match

Instructions: Cut out the cards on the dotted line. Give one card to each student. Distribute cards in sequence so for every student with a Contraction card, there is a student with a matching Words card.

CONTRACTiONS

What two words make this contraction?

don't

Contraction

CONTRACTiONS

What contraction do these two words make?

do not

Words

CONTRACTiONS

What word make this contraction?

can't

Contraction

CONTRACTiONS

What contraction does this word make?

cannot

Words

CONTRACTiONS

What two words make this contraction?

I'm

Contraction

CONTRACTiONS

What contraction do these two words make?

I am

Words

CONTRACTIONS
Mix-N-Match

Instructions: Cut out the cards on the dotted line. Give one card to each student. Distribute cards in sequence so for every student with a Contraction card, there is a student with a matching Words card.

CONTRACTIONS

What two words make this contraction?

she's

Contraction

CONTRACTIONS

What contraction do these two words make?

she is

Words

CONTRACTIONS

What two words make this contraction?

I've

Contraction

CONTRACTIONS

What contraction do these two words make?

I have

Words

CONTRACTIONS

What two words make this contraction?

won't

Contraction

CONTRACTIONS

What contraction do these two words make?

will not

Words

Cooperative Learning & Grammar
Kagan Publishing • 1 (800) 933-2667 • www.KaganOnline.com

Instructions: Cut out the cards on the dotted line. Give one card to each student. Distribute cards in sequence so for every student with a Contraction card, there is a student with a matching Words card.

CONTRACTiONS

What two words
make this contraction?

didn't

Contraction

CONTRACTiONS

What contraction do
these two words make?

did not

Words

CONTRACTiONS

What two words
make this contraction?

couldn't

Contraction

CONTRACTiONS

What contraction do
these two words make?

could not

Words

CONTRACTiONS

What two words
make this contraction?

I'll

Contraction

CONTRACTiONS

What contraction do
these two words make?

I will

Words

CONTRACTIONS
Mix-N-Match

Instructions: Cut out the cards on the dotted line. Give one card to each student. Distribute cards in sequence so for every student with a Contraction card, there is a student with a matching Words card.

CONTRACTIONS

What two words make this contraction?

doesn't

Contraction

CONTRACTIONS

What contraction do these two words make?

does not

Words

CONTRACTIONS

What two words make this contraction?

he's

Contraction

CONTRACTIONS

What contraction do these two words make?

he is

Words

CONTRACTIONS

What two words make this contraction?

shouldn't

Contraction

CONTRACTIONS

What contraction do these two words make?

should not

Words

Cooperative Learning & Grammar
Kagan Publishing • 1 (800) 933-2667 • www.KaganOnline.com

CONTRACTIONS
Mix-N-Match

Instructions: Cut out the cards on the dotted line. Give one card to each student. Distribute cards in sequence so for every student with a Contraction card, there is a student with a matching Words card.

CONTRACTiONS

What two words make this contraction?

we've

Contraction

CONTRACTiONS

What contraction do these two words make?

we have

Words

CONTRACTiONS

What two words make this contraction?

could've

Contraction

CONTRACTiONS

What contraction do these two words make?

could have

Words

CONTRACTiONS

What two words make this contraction?

wouldn't

Contraction

CONTRACTiONS

What contraction do these two words make?

would not

Words

CONTRACTIONS
Mix-N-Match

Instructions: Cut out the cards on the dotted line. Give one card to each student. Distribute cards in sequence so for every student with a Contraction card, there is a student with a matching Words card.

CONTRACTIONS

What two words
make this contraction?

he's

Contraction

CONTRACTIONS

What contraction do
these two words make?

he is

Words

CONTRACTIONS

What two words
make this contraction?

wasn't

Contraction

CONTRACTIONS

What contraction do
these two words make?

was not

Words

CONTRACTIONS

What two words
make this contraction?

haven't

Contraction

CONTRACTIONS

What contraction do
these two words make?

have not

Words

Cooperative Learning & Grammar
Kagan Publishing • 1 (800) 933-2667 • www.KaganOnline.com

Instructions: Cut out each card along the dotted line. Then fold each card in half so the question is on one side and the answer is on the back. Glue or tape the cards together to keep the answers and questions on opposite sides.

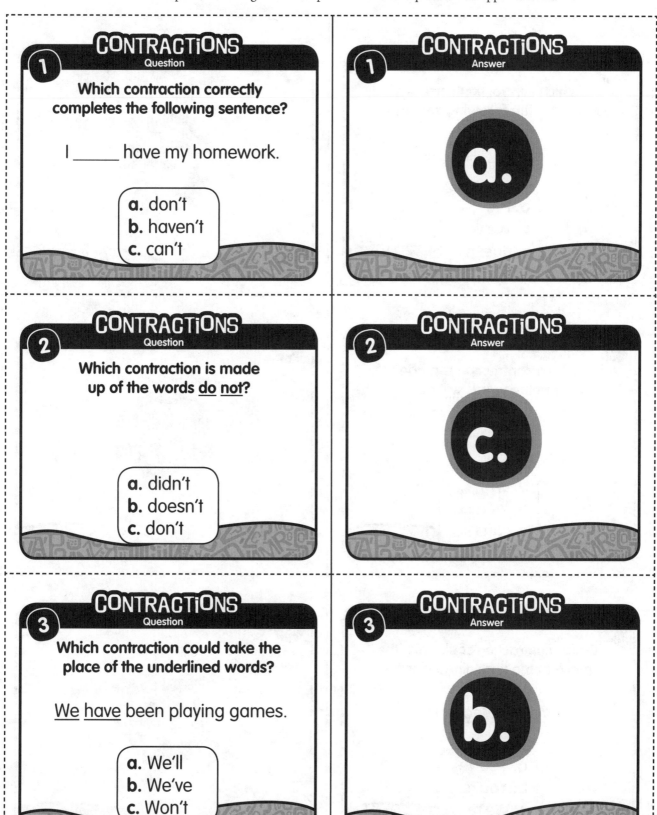

CONTRACTIONS
Question

1 Which contraction correctly completes the following sentence?

I _____ have my homework.

a. don't
b. haven't
c. can't

CONTRACTIONS
Answer

1 a.

CONTRACTIONS
Question

2 Which contraction is made up of the words <u>do</u> <u>not</u>?

a. didn't
b. doesn't
c. don't

CONTRACTIONS
Answer

2 c.

CONTRACTIONS
Question

3 Which contraction could take the place of the underlined words?

<u>We</u> <u>have</u> been playing games.

a. We'll
b. We've
c. Won't

CONTRACTIONS
Answer

3 b.

Instructions: Cut out each card along the dotted line. Then fold each card in half so the question is on one side and the answer is on the back. Glue or tape the cards together to keep the answers and questions on opposite sides.

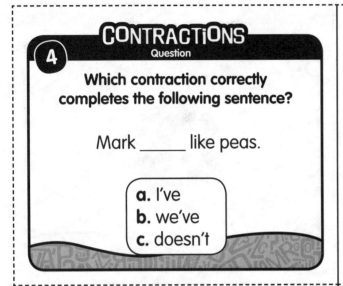

CONTRACTIONS
Question

4

Which contraction correctly completes the following sentence?

Mark _____ like peas.

a. I've
b. we've
c. doesn't

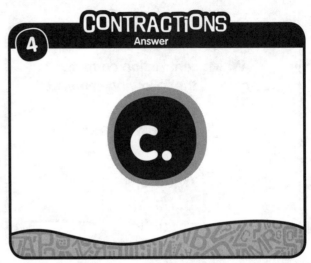

CONTRACTIONS
Answer

4

c.

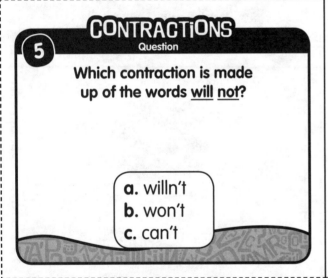

CONTRACTIONS
Question

5

Which contraction is made up of the words <u>will</u> <u>not</u>?

a. willn't
b. won't
c. can't

CONTRACTIONS
Answer

5

b.

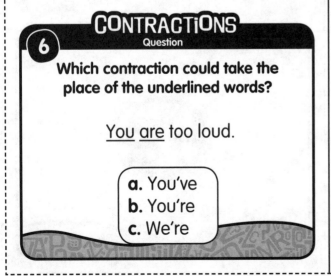

CONTRACTIONS
Question

6

Which contraction could take the place of the underlined words?

<u>You</u> <u>are</u> too loud.

a. You've
b. You're
c. We're

CONTRACTIONS
Answer

6

b.

Cooperative Learning & Grammar
Kagan Publishing • 1 (800) 933-2667 • www.KaganOnline.com

Instructions: Cut out each card along the dotted line. Then fold each card in half so the question is on one side and the answer is on the back. Glue or tape the cards together to keep the answers and questions on opposite sides.

CONTRACTIONS
Question

7

Which contraction correctly completes the following sentence?

Mom and Dad said _____ watch me.

a. we've
b. can't
c. they'll

CONTRACTIONS
Answer

7

c.

CONTRACTIONS
Question

8

Which contraction is made up of the words <u>did not</u>?

a. doesn't
b. didn't
c. don't

CONTRACTIONS
Answer

8

b.

CONTRACTIONS
Question

9

Which contraction could take the place of the underlined words?

Susie <u>will</u> <u>not</u> be at school.

a. wouldn't
b. can't
c. won't

CONTRACTIONS
Answer

9

c.

Instructions: Cut out each card along the dotted line. Then fold each card in half so the question is on one side and the answer is on the back. Glue or tape the cards together to keep the answers and questions on opposite sides.

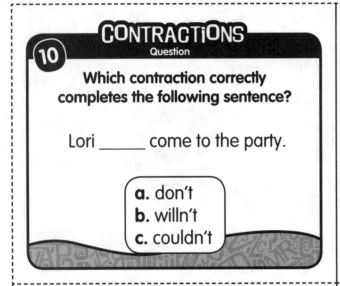

CONTRACTIONS
Question

10

Which contraction correctly completes the following sentence?

Lori _____ come to the party.

a. don't
b. willn't
c. couldn't

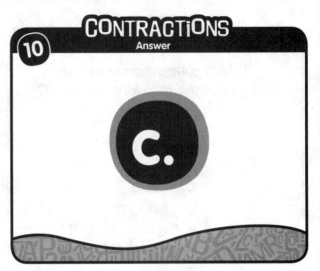

CONTRACTIONS
Answer

10

c.

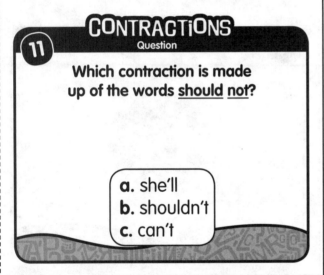

CONTRACTIONS
Question

11

Which contraction is made up of the words <u>should</u> <u>not</u>?

a. she'll
b. shouldn't
c. can't

CONTRACTIONS
Answer

11

b.

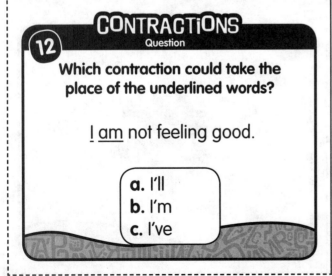

CONTRACTIONS
Question

12

Which contraction could take the place of the underlined words?

<u>I am</u> not feeling good.

a. I'll
b. I'm
c. I've

CONTRACTIONS
Answer

12

b.

Cooperative Learning & Grammar
Kagan Publishing • 1 (800) 933-2667 • www.KaganOnline.com

CONTRACTIONS
Quiz-Quiz-Trade

Instructions: Cut out each card along the dotted line. Then fold each card in half so the question is on one side and the answer is on the back. Glue or tape the cards together to keep the answers and questions on opposite sides.

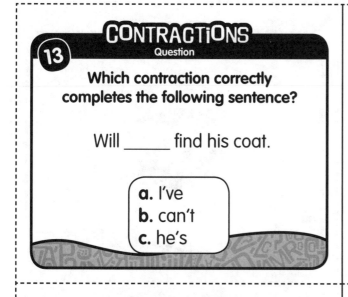

CONTRACTIONS
Question

13

Which contraction correctly completes the following sentence?

Will _____ find his coat.

a. I've
b. can't
c. he's

CONTRACTIONS
Answer

13

b.

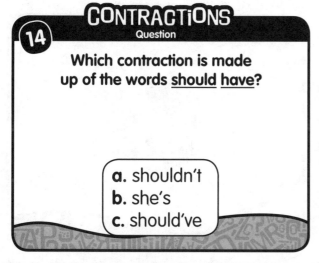

CONTRACTIONS
Question

14

Which contraction is made up of the words <u>should</u> <u>have</u>?

a. shouldn't
b. she's
c. should've

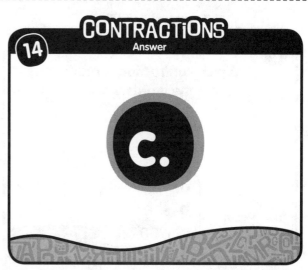

CONTRACTIONS
Answer

14

c.

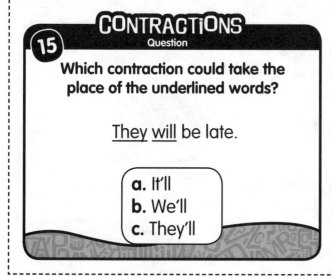

CONTRACTIONS
Question

15

Which contraction could take the place of the underlined words?

<u>They</u> <u>will</u> be late.

a. It'll
b. We'll
c. They'll

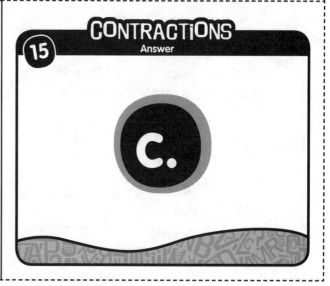

CONTRACTIONS
Answer

15

c.

CONTRACTIONS
Quiz-Quiz-Trade

Instructions: Cut out each card along the dotted line. Then fold each card in half so the question is on one side and the answer is on the back. Glue or tape the cards together to keep the answers and questions on opposite sides.

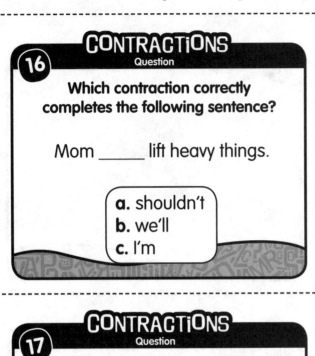

CONTRACTIONS
Question

16

Which contraction correctly completes the following sentence?

Mom _____ lift heavy things.

a. shouldn't
b. we'll
c. I'm

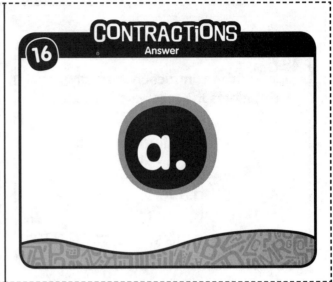

CONTRACTIONS
Answer

16

a.

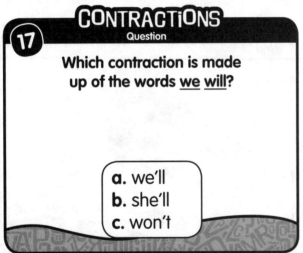

CONTRACTIONS
Question

17

Which contraction is made up of the words <u>we will</u>?

a. we'll
b. she'll
c. won't

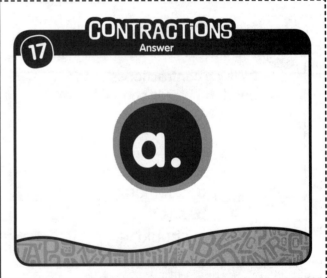

CONTRACTIONS
Answer

17

a.

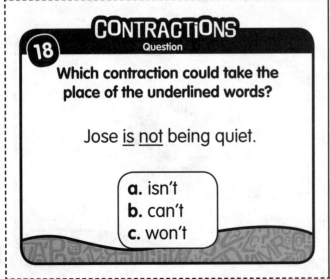

CONTRACTIONS
Question

18

Which contraction could take the place of the underlined words?

Jose <u>is</u> <u>not</u> being quiet.

a. isn't
b. can't
c. won't

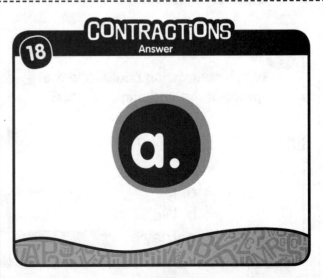

CONTRACTIONS
Answer

18

a.

Cooperative Learning & Grammar
Kagan Publishing • 1 (800) 933-2667 • www.KaganOnline.com

PUNCTUATION

Grammar Skills 3
PUNCTUATION

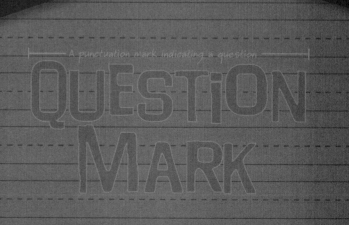

Question Mark

QUESTION MARK

KEY IDEA All sentences begin with a capital letter.

Example: The house is blue.

Instructions: Write the sentence with the correct capitalization. Take turns working with your partner to solve the problems using RallyCoach or Sage-N-Scribe.

PARTNER A

Name _____

1 it is time to go home.

_____

_____

2 my dog is named Fido.

_____

_____

3 when can I dance?

_____

_____

4 do not forget a coat.

_____

_____

PARTNER B

Name _____

1 my teddy bear is black.

_____

_____

2 the picture is very pretty.

_____

_____

3 his sister is crying.

_____

_____

4 the dancer is stunning.

_____

_____

Cooperative Learning & Grammar
Kagan Publishing • 1 (800) 933-2667 • www.KaganOnline.com

CAPITAL LETTERS—DAYS OF THE WEEK
Find Someone Who

Name _____

Instructions: Pair up and take turns identifying the day of the week with the pictures below. Don't forget to get your partner's initials.

DAYS OF THE WEEK

Monday

Tuesday
LIBRARY

Wednesday

Thursday

Friday

Saturday

Sunday

1 Susie was riding her bike on

_____.

Initials

2 Susie went to the library on

_____.

Initials

3 Susie played on the computer on

_____.

Initials

4 Susie walked her dog on

_____.

Initials

5 Susie did the dishes on

_____.

Initials

6 Susie did her homework on

_____.

Initials

Instructions: Copy one set of cards for each team. Cut out each card along the dotted line. Give each team a set of cards to play Fan-N-Pick or Showdown.

CAPITAL LETTERS

1 Rewrite the sentence. Correct the name.

officer john visited our classroom.

CAPITAL LETTERS

2 Rewrite the day correctly.

saturday

CAPITAL LETTERS

3 Rewrite the sentence. Correct the name.

We live on planet earth.

CAPITAL LETTERS

4 Rewrite the city name correctly.

new york

CAPITAL LETTERS

5 Rewrite the restaurant name correctly.

pizza hut®

CAPITAL LETTERS

6 Rewrite the sentence. Correct the restaurant name.

i went to burger king® for lunch.

Cooperative Learning & Grammar
Kagan Publishing • 1 (800) 933-2667 • www.KaganOnline.com

CAPITAL LETTERS
Fan-N-Pick/Showdown

Instructions: Copy one set of cards for each team. Cut out each card along the dotted line. Give each team a set of cards to play Fan-N-Pick or Showdown.

CAPITAL LETTERS

7

Rewrite the sentence.
Correct the month.

i was born
in october.

CAPITAL LETTERS

8

Rewrite the sentence.
Correct the name.

i live on bird lane.

CAPITAL LETTERS

9

Rewrite the city name correctly.

chicago, illinois

CAPITAL LETTERS

10

Rewrite the sentence.
Correct the name.

we went to stockstill
park for a field trip.

CAPITAL LETTERS

11

Rewrite the sentence.
Correct the book name.

mary read
goodnight moon.

CAPITAL LETTERS

12

Rewrite the name correctly.

valentine's day

CAPITAL LETTERS
Quiz-Quiz-Trade

Instructions: Cut out each card along the dotted line. Then fold each card in half so the question is on one side and the answer is on the back. Glue or tape the cards together to keep the answers and questions on opposite sides.

CAPITAL LETTERS
Question

1 Which noun should be capitalized?

a. dog

b. sister

c. missouri

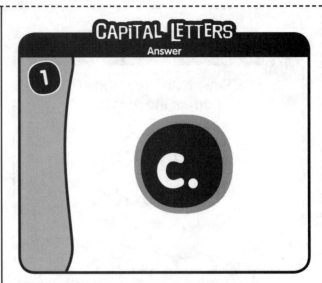

CAPITAL LETTERS
Answer

1 c.

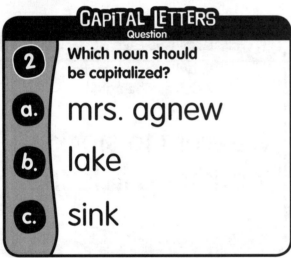

CAPITAL LETTERS
Question

2 Which noun should be capitalized?

a. mrs. agnew

b. lake

c. sink

CAPITAL LETTERS
Answer

2 a.

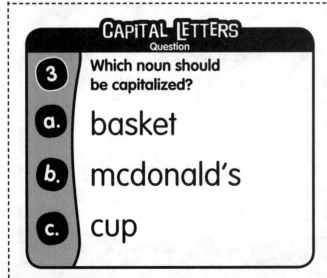

CAPITAL LETTERS
Question

3 Which noun should be capitalized?

a. basket

b. mcdonald's

c. cup

CAPITAL LETTERS
Answer

3 b.

Cooperative Learning & Grammar
Kagan Publishing • 1 (800) 933-2667 • www.KaganOnline.com

CAPITAL LETTERS
Quiz-Quiz-Trade

Instructions: Cut out each card along the dotted line. Then fold each card in half so the question is on one side and the answer is on the back. Glue or tape the cards together to keep the answers and questions on opposite sides.

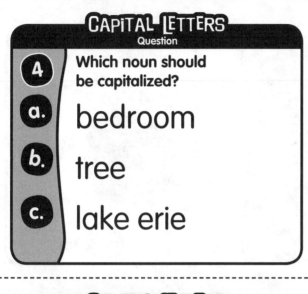

CAPITAL LETTERS
Question

4 Which noun should be capitalized?

a. bedroom

b. tree

c. lake erie

CAPITAL LETTERS
Answer

4

c.

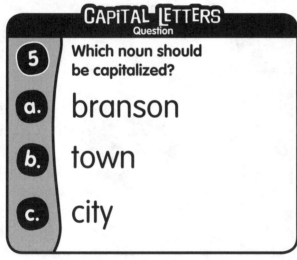

CAPITAL LETTERS
Question

5 Which noun should be capitalized?

a. branson

b. town

c. city

CAPITAL LETTERS
Answer

5

a.

CAPITAL LETTERS
Question

6 Which noun should be capitalized?

a. girl

b. sister

c. susie

CAPITAL LETTERS
Answer

6

c.

CAPITAL LETTERS
Quiz-Quiz-Trade

Instructions: Cut out each card along the dotted line. Then fold each card in half so the question is on one side and the answer is on the back. Glue or tape the cards together to keep the answers and questions on opposite sides.

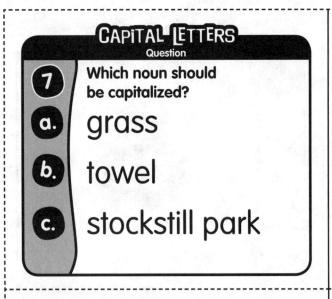

CAPITAL LETTERS
Question

7 Which noun should be capitalized?

a. grass

b. towel

c. stockstill park

CAPITAL LETTERS
Answer

7

c.

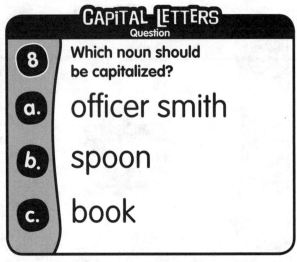

CAPITAL LETTERS
Question

8 Which noun should be capitalized?

a. officer smith

b. spoon

c. book

CAPITAL LETTERS
Answer

8

a.

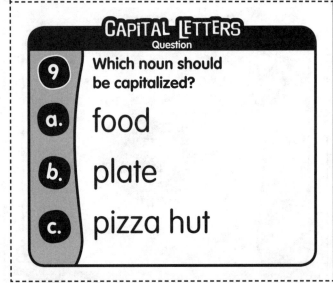

CAPITAL LETTERS
Question

9 Which noun should be capitalized?

a. food

b. plate

c. pizza hut

CAPITAL LETTERS
Answer

9

c.

Cooperative Learning & Grammar
Kagan Publishing • 1 (800) 933-2667 • www.KaganOnline.com

CAPITAL LETTERS
Quiz-Quiz-Trade

Instructions: Cut out each card along the dotted line. Then fold each card in half so the question is on one side and the answer is on the back. Glue or tape the cards together to keep the answers and questions on opposite sides.

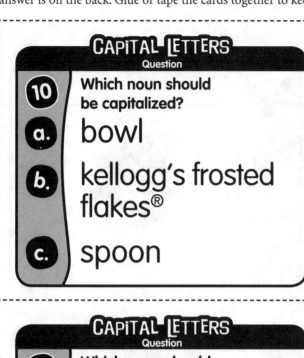

CAPITAL LETTERS
Question

10 Which noun should be capitalized?

a. bowl

b. kellogg's frosted flakes®

c. spoon

CAPITAL LETTERS
Answer

10

b.

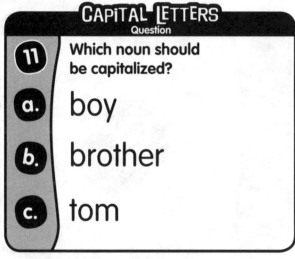

CAPITAL LETTERS
Question

11 Which noun should be capitalized?

a. boy

b. brother

c. tom

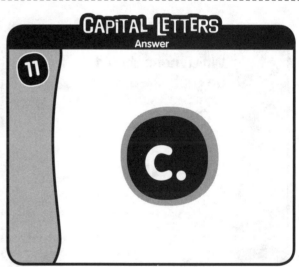

CAPITAL LETTERS
Answer

11

c.

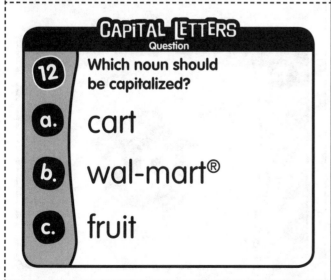

CAPITAL LETTERS
Question

12 Which noun should be capitalized?

a. cart

b. wal-mart®

c. fruit

CAPITAL LETTERS
Answer

12

b.

Cooperative Learning & Grammar
Kagan Publishing • 1 (800) 933-2667 • www.KaganOnline.com

CAPITAL LETTERS
Quiz-Quiz-Trade

Instructions: Cut out each card along the dotted line. Then fold each card in half so the question is on one side and the answer is on the back. Glue or tape the cards together to keep the answers and questions on opposite sides.

CAPITAL LETTERS
Question

13 Which noun should be capitalized?

a. ice cream

b. banana

c. st. louis

CAPITAL LETTERS
Answer

13

c.

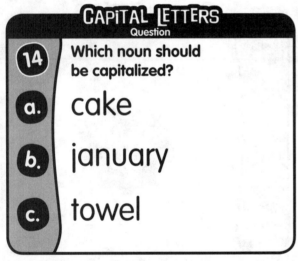

CAPITAL LETTERS
Question

14 Which noun should be capitalized?

a. cake

b. january

c. towel

CAPITAL LETTERS
Answer

14

b.

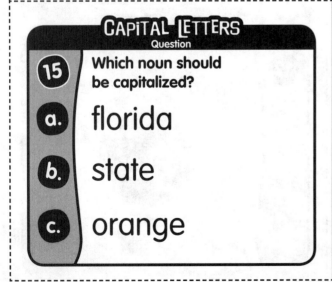

CAPITAL LETTERS
Question

15 Which noun should be capitalized?

a. florida

b. state

c. orange

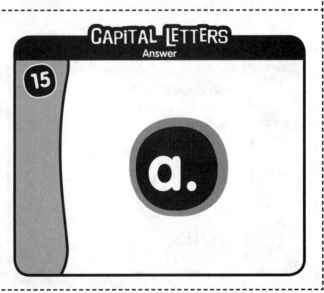

CAPITAL LETTERS
Answer

15

a.

Cooperative Learning & Grammar
Kagan Publishing • 1 (800) 933-2667 • www.KaganOnline.com

Instructions: Cut out each card along the dotted line. Then fold each card in half so the question is on one side and the answer is on the back. Glue or tape the cards together to keep the answers and questions on opposite sides.

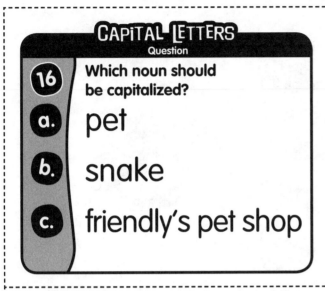

CAPITAL LETTERS
Question

16 Which noun should be capitalized?
a. pet
b. snake
c. friendly's pet shop

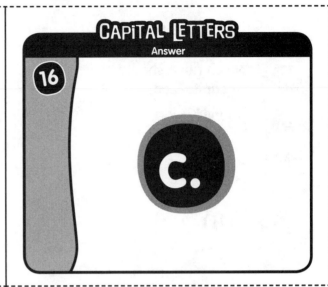

CAPITAL LETTERS
Answer

16 c.

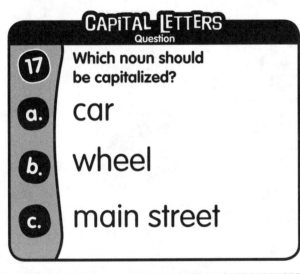

CAPITAL LETTERS
Question

17 Which noun should be capitalized?
a. car
b. wheel
c. main street

CAPITAL LETTERS
Answer

17 c.

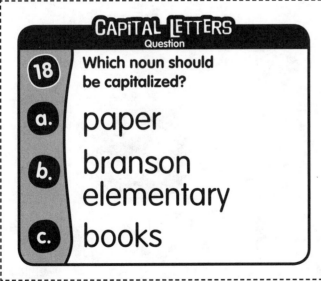

CAPITAL LETTERS
Question

18 Which noun should be capitalized?
a. paper
b. branson elementary
c. books

CAPITAL LETTERS
Answer

18 b.

Instructions: Cut out each card along the dotted line. Then fold each card in half so the question is on one side and the answer is on the back. Glue or tape the cards together to keep the answers and questions on opposite sides.

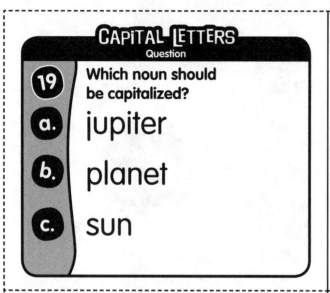

CAPITAL LETTERS
Question

19 Which noun should be capitalized?

a. jupiter

b. planet

c. sun

CAPITAL LETTERS
Answer

19

a.

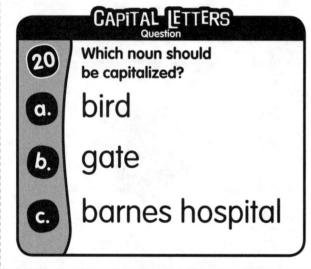

CAPITAL LETTERS
Question

20 Which noun should be capitalized?

a. bird

b. gate

c. barnes hospital

CAPITAL LETTERS
Answer

20

c.

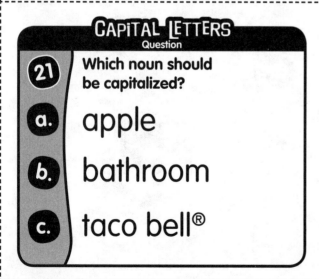

CAPITAL LETTERS
Question

21 Which noun should be capitalized?

a. apple

b. bathroom

c. taco bell®

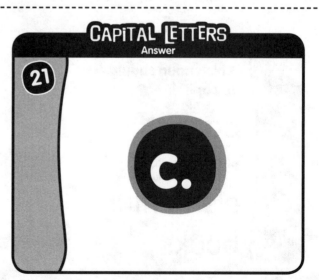

CAPITAL LETTERS
Answer

21

c.

Cooperative Learning & Grammar
Kagan Publishing • 1 (800) 933-2667 • www.KaganOnline.com

Instructions: Cut out each card along the dotted line. Then fold each card in half so the question is on one side and the answer is on the back. Glue or tape the cards together to keep the answers and questions on opposite sides.

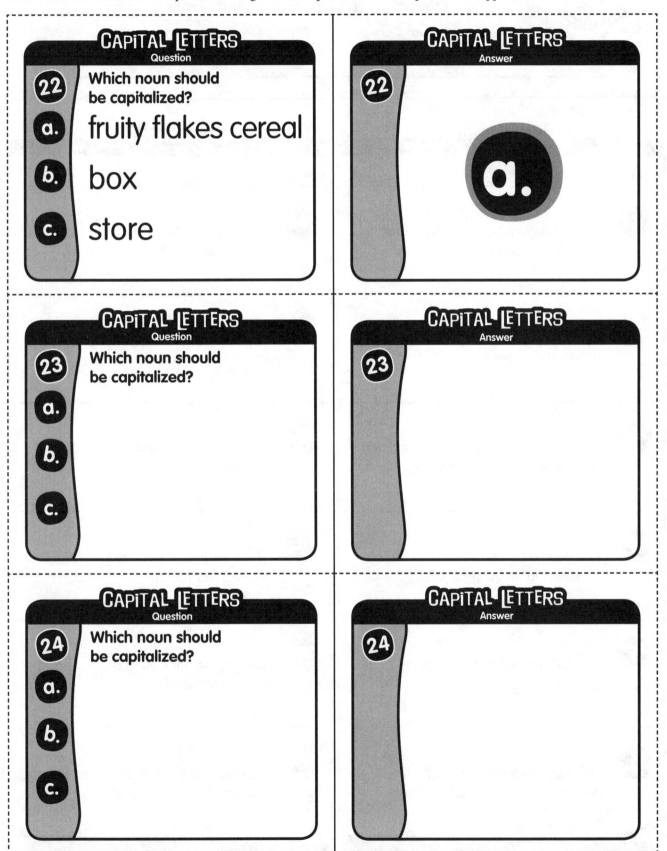

CAPITAL LETTERS
Question

22 Which noun should be capitalized?

a. fruity flakes cereal

b. box

c. store

CAPITAL LETTERS
Answer

22

a.

CAPITAL LETTERS
Question

23 Which noun should be capitalized?

a.

b.

c.

CAPITAL LETTERS
Answer

23

CAPITAL LETTERS
Question

24 Which noun should be capitalized?

a.

b.

c.

CAPITAL LETTERS
Answer

24

 COMMAS IN A LIST
RallyCoach/Sage-N-Scribe

 KEY IDEA

Commas are used to separate items in a list. As readers, we pause when we see commas so it is important to include them in your writing.

Example: Johnny wants to play baseball, basketball, and tennis this year in school.

↑ ↑
Commas

Instructions: In the sentences below, add commas in the correct locations. Take turns working with your partner to solve the problems using RallyCoach or Sage-N-Scribe.

PARTNER A

Name _____

1 Megan brought cookies cake and soda to the party.

2 Karen bought a teddy bear doll and purse at the store.

3 Kolby picked up his movies put away his clothes and made his bed.

4 My favorite books are about animals people and faraway places.

5 My dad made tacos burritos and salad for dinner.

6 I packed my towel swimsuit bucket and umbrella for my beach party.

PARTNER B

Name _____

1 Caleb's favorite foods are ice cream pizza and carrots.

2 My bedroom has a new bed bookshelf and rug.

3 I have math spelling and reading homework to do tonight.

4 The doctor checked my toes legs and knees after my fall.

5 We got the new kitten a pillow food and water bowl.

6 Jessica took her pajamas blanket and slippers to the sleepover.

Cooperative Learning & Grammar
Kagan Publishing • 1 (800) 933-2667 • www.KaganOnline.com

Commas in Dates & Places
RallyCoach/Sage-N-Scribe

KEY IDEAS

When you write a date, you place a comma after the day of the week and before the year.

Example: Monday, September 17, 1983   or   July 16, 2008

When you write a city and state, you place a comma after the city but before the state.

Example: Chillicothe, Missouri

Instructions: Write in the commas where they belong in the dates and places below. Take turns working with your partner to solve the problems using RallyCoach or Sage-N-Scribe.

	PARTNER A		PARTNER B
Name		Name	
1	March 10 1978	**1**	Mason Ohio
2	Murfeesburo Arkansas	**2**	Monday February 1 1958
3	Sunday December 27 2011	**3**	Colorado Springs Colorado
4	Lake Tahoe California	**4**	June 23 2007

COMMAS
Find Someone Who

Name _____

Instructions: Pair up and take turns answering the questions below. Don't forget to get your partner's initials.

1

Which sentence has commas in the correct place?

a. January 4, 1980

b. January, 4 1980

c. January 4 1980

Initials

2

Which sentence has commas in the correct place?

a. I live in Branson M,O.

b. I live in Branson, MO.

c. I live in, Branson MO.

Initials

3

Which sentence has commas in the correct place?

a. Joe brought books paper and pencils.

b. Joe brought books, paper and pencils.

c. Joe brought books, paper, and pencils.

Initials

4

Which sentence has commas in the correct place?

a. We took our vacation, in Springfield Illinois.

b. We took our vacation in Springfield Illinois.

c. We took our vacation in Springfield, Illinois.

Initials

5

Which sentence has commas in the correct place?

a. Dear, Grandma

b. Dear Gra,ndma

c. Dear Grandma,

Initials

6

Which sentence has commas in the correct place?

a. Your, daughter

b. Y,our daughter

c. Your daughter,

Initials

Cooperative Learning & Grammar
Kagan Publishing • 1 (800) 933-2667 • www.KaganOnline.com

Name _____

Instructions: Pair up and take turns putting commas in the correct places and answering questions in the sentences below. Don't forget to get your partner's initials.

---

1 Rewrite the date correctly.

january 6 2011

_____

Initials

---

2 Rewrite the date correctly.

march 2 1990

_____

Initials

---

3 Rewrite the date correctly.

april 8 1970

_____

Initials

---

4 Which date below is written correctly?

(a.) December 6 1980,

(b.) December 6, 1980

(c.) december 6, 1980

Initials

---

5 Rewrite the date correctly.

october 10 2010

_____

Initials

---

6 Which date below is written correctly?

(a.) august, 3 1997

(b.) August 3 1997

(c.) August 3, 1997

Initials

---

7 Rewrite the date correctly.

july 17 2009

_____

Initials

---

8 Which date below is written correctly?

(a.) May 5, 2009

(b.) may 5, 2009

(c.) May 5 2009

Initials

---

9 Rewrite the date correctly.

november 25, 2012

_____

Initials

Instructions: Copy one set of cards for each team. Cut out each card along the dotted line. Give each team a set of cards to play Fan-N-Pick or Showdown.

COMMAS

1 Rewrite the sentence with the commas in the correct place.

I live in Austin Texas.

COMMAS

2 Rewrite the sentence with the commas in the correct place.

I was born on January 12 2004.

COMMAS

3 Rewrite the closing of a letter with the commas in the correct place.

Yours truly

COMMAS

4 Rewrite the sentence with the commas in the correct place.

I like to read write and play games.

COMMAS

5 Rewrite the sentence with the commas in the correct place.

My dog can catch sticks balls and newspapers.

COMMAS

6 Rewrite the greeting of a letter with the commas in the correct place.

Dear Grandma

Instructions: Copy one set of cards for each team. Cut out each card along the dotted line. Give each team a set of cards to play Fan-N-Pick or Showdown.

COMMAS

7 Rewrite the sentence with the commas in the correct place.

We will be going to St. Louis Missouri for vacation.

COMMAS

8 Rewrite the sentence with the commas in the correct place.

Maria brought cupcakes plates and cups to the party.

COMMAS

9 Rewrite the sentence with the commas in the correct place.

Please bring yarn glue and crayons to the carpet.

COMMAS

10 Rewrite the sentence with the commas in the correct place.

The last day of school is May 22 2013.

COMMAS

11 Rewrite the closing of a letter with the commas in the correct place.

Your Daughter

COMMAS

12 Rewrite the greeting of a letter with the commas in the correct place.

Dear Mr. President

ENDING PUNCTUATION
RallyCoach/Sage-N-Scribe

Instructions: In the sentences below, add the correct ending punctuation from the Punctuation Bank. Take turns working with your partner to solve the problems using RallyCoach or Sage-N-Scribe.

PARTNER A	PARTNER B

PUNCTUATION BANK . ? !

Name _____   Name _____

Partner A	Partner B
1 Sloan loves to eat_____	1 The bird is chirping_____
2 The rain is pouring_____	2 Can you get the phone_____
3 Where are my shoes_____	3 Do not feed the bears_____
4 Close the door tightly_____	4 Way to go team_____
5 The sun is shinning_____	5 My shirt is too big_____
6 It is freezing outside_____	6 Turn down the radio_____

Cooperative Learning & Grammar
Kagan Publishing • 1 (800) 933-2667 • www.KaganOnline.com

PUNCTUATION
Find Someone Who

Name _____

Instructions: Pair up and take turns putting either a "." (period) or a "?" (question mark) to correctly complete each sentence below. Don't forget to get your partner's initials.

1 Do you like pizza _____   Initials

2 My mom will pick us up at four o'clock _____   Initials

3 When can we go to the park _____   Initials

4 Olive's birthday is on Saturday _____   Initials

5 Bring your books to the carpet _____   Initials

6 Did you enjoy the play _____   Initials

7 Make your bed _____   Initials

8 Math is my favorite subject _____   Initials

9 Where are you going _____   Initials

PUNCTUATION
Fan-N-Pick/Showdown

Instructions: Copy one set of cards for each team. Cut out each card along the dotted line. Give each team a set of cards to play Fan-N-Pick or Showdown.

PUNCTUATION

1 Choose the punctuation that completes the sentence.

Get out your math book ___

a. .
b. ?
c. !

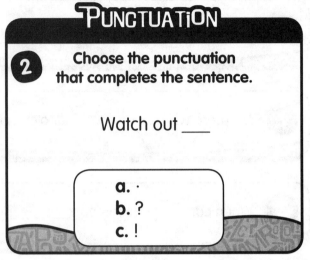

PUNCTUATION

2 Choose the punctuation that completes the sentence.

Watch out ___

a. .
b. ?
c. !

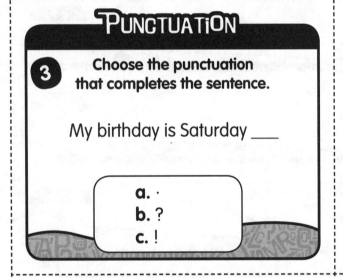

PUNCTUATION

3 Choose the punctuation that completes the sentence.

My birthday is Saturday ___

a. .
b. ?
c. !

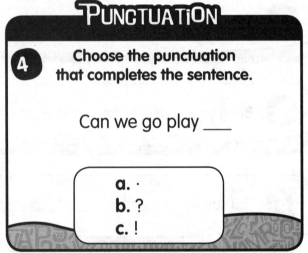

PUNCTUATION

4 Choose the punctuation that completes the sentence.

Can we go play ___

a. .
b. ?
c. !

PUNCTUATION

5 Choose the punctuation that completes the sentence.

Wow ___

a. .
b. ?
c. !

PUNCTUATION

6 Choose the punctuation that completes the sentence.

What time is lunch ___

a. .
b. ?
c. !

Cooperative Learning & Grammar
Kagan Publishing • 1 (800) 933-2667 • www.KaganOnline.com

Instructions: Copy one set of cards for each team. Cut out each card along the dotted line. Give each team a set of cards to play Fan-N-Pick or Showdown.

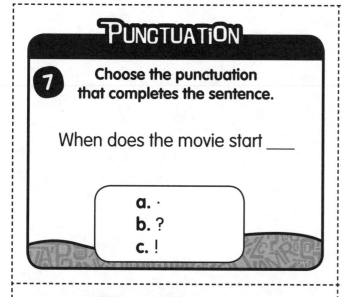

PUNCTUATION

7 Choose the punctuation that completes the sentence.

When does the movie start ___

a. .
b. ?
c. !

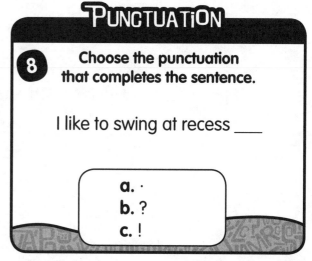

PUNCTUATION

8 Choose the punctuation that completes the sentence.

I like to swing at recess ___

a. .
b. ?
c. !

PUNCTUATION

9 Choose the punctuation that completes the sentence.

Oh my ___

a. .
b. ?
c. !

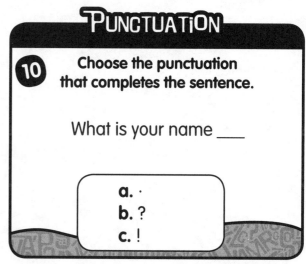

PUNCTUATION

10 Choose the punctuation that completes the sentence.

What is your name ___

a. .
b. ?
c. !

PUNCTUATION

11 Choose the punctuation that completes the sentence.

Practice starts at five o'clock ___

a. .
b. ?
c. !

PUNCTUATION

12 Choose the punctuation that completes the sentence.

Pam collects stamps ___

a. .
b. ?
c. !

Grammar Skills 4

SENTENCES

asking
exclamation
statement

COMPLETE SENTENCES
RallyCoach/Sage-N-Scribe

KEY IDEA

A complete sentence has a naming and telling part.

NOT a sentence:
Duck swim.
T.V. broken.

Complete sentence:
The duck swims in the water.
The T.V. is broken.

Instructions: Take turns working with your partner to identify the sentence as either complete or not complete. Circle the correct answer. Use RallyCoach or Sage-N-Scribe to solve the problem.

PARTNER A

Name _____

1 My shoe is not tied.

Complete   Not Complete

2 Boy sad.

Complete   Not Complete

3 It time lunch.

Complete   Not Complete

4 Daniel kicked the ball.

Complete   Not Complete

5 To the store.

Complete   Not Complete

PARTNER A

Name _____

1 Down the street.

Complete   Not Complete

2 The truck is on the road.

Complete   Not Complete

3 After a while.

Complete   Not Complete

4 The police officer waved.

Complete   Not Complete

5 Time to go.

Complete   Not Complete

Cooperative Learning & Grammar
Kagan Publishing • 1 (800) 933-2667 • www.KaganOnline.com

COMPLETE SENTENCES
RallyCoach/Sage-N-Scribe

Instructions: Take turns working with your partner to choose the word to complete the sentence. Fill in the correct answer on the blank lines. Use RallyCoach or Sage-N-Scribe to solve the problem.

PARTNER A	PARTNER B

Name _____ **Name** _____

1 The _____ rolled down the street.

ball   boy   flower

1 The _____ drove to the store.

book   car   piano

2 The _____ blew in the wind.

car   leaf   house

2 The _____ hopped in the field.

duck   rabbit   flower

3 The _____ rang loudly.

duck   phone   piano

3 The mom cleaned the _____.

house   leaf   tree

4 The teacher read a _____.

violin   rabbit   book

7 The _____ scraped his knee.

car   phone   boy

 COMPLETE SENTENCES
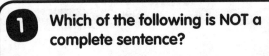 Find-N-Fix

Name _____

Instructions: For each problem, find the incorrect sentence. Indicate which is incorrect using your Find-N-Fix cards. When your team agrees, fix the incomplete sentence in the box.

1 **Which of the following is NOT a complete sentence?**

a. Megan likes chocolate milk.

b. Kolby kick.

c. My book is good.

Complete the Sentence

2 **Which of the following is NOT a complete sentence?**

a. Down the street.

b. Please sing loudly.

c. The rug is green.

Complete the Sentence

3 **Which of the following is NOT a complete sentence?**

a. Najem loves to read.

b. Marrin is my niece.

c. In December.

Complete the Sentence

4 **Which of the following is NOT a complete sentence?**

a. Up in the air.

b. The sky is blue.

c. My favorite sport is football.

Complete the Sentence

Cooperative Learning & Grammar
Kagan Publishing • 1 (800) 933-2667 • www.KaganOnline.com

COMPLETE SENTENCES
Find Someone Who

Name _____

Instructions: Pair up and take turns identifying if the sentence below is complete or incomplete. Don't forget to get your partner's initials.

Is this sentence complete?	Yes/No	Initials
1 Jarrod ran.	Yes No	
2 The car is new.	Yes No	
3 To the store.	Yes No	
4 Fell down.	Yes No	
5 The boy is asleep.	Yes No	
6 The tent is full.	Yes No	
7 The ball is flat.	Yes No	
8 Under the bed.	Yes No	
9 I am hungry.	Yes No	

COMPLETE SENTENCES
Fan-N-Pick/Showdown

Instructions: Copy one set of cards for each team. Cut out each card along the dotted line. Give each team a set of cards to play Fan-N-Pick or Showdown.

COMPLETE SENTENCES

1

Fill in the blank to fix the incomplete sentence.

_____ to turn in your homework.

COMPLETE SENTENCES

2

Fill in the blank to fix the incomplete sentence.

_____ to the store.

COMPLETE SENTENCES

3

Fill in the blank to fix the incomplete sentence.

_____ off the stove.

COMPLETE SENTENCES

4

Fill in the blank to fix the incomplete sentence.

The boy kicked _____.

COMPLETE SENTENCES

5

Fill in the blank to fix the incomplete sentence.

The cat jumped _____.

COMPLETE SENTENCES

6

Fill in the blank to fix the incomplete sentence.

Jason asked me to _____.

Cooperative Learning & Grammar
Kagan Publishing • 1 (800) 933-2667 • www.KaganOnline.com

Instructions: Copy one set of cards for each team. Cut out each card along the dotted line. Give each team a set of cards to play Fan-N-Pick or Showdown.

COMPLETE SENTENCES

7

Fill in the blank to fix
the incomplete sentence.

Larry caught

_____ .

COMPLETE SENTENCES

8

Fill in the blank to fix
the incomplete sentence.

Ms. Hackman is

_____ .

COMPLETE SENTENCES

9

Fill in the blank to fix
the incomplete sentence.

Pirates like

_____ .

COMPLETE SENTENCES

10

Fill in the blank to fix
the incomplete sentence.

I finally got

_____ .

COMPLETE SENTENCES

11

Fill in the blank to fix
the incomplete sentence.

_____ down
the street.

COMPLETE SENTENCES

12

Fill in the blank to fix
the incomplete sentence.

_____ in
the glass.

COMPLETE SENTENCES
Quiz-Quiz-Trade

Instructions: Cut out each card along the dotted line. Then fold each card in half so the question is on one side and the answer is on the back. Glue or tape the cards together to keep the answers and questions on opposite sides.

COMPLETE SENTENCES
Question

1

Is the sentence a complete sentence?

Kolby likes to play with his toy cars.

Yes or No

COMPLETE SENTENCES
Answer

1

Yes

COMPLETE SENTENCES
Question

2

Is the sentence a complete sentence?

To the park to play on the monkey bars.

Yes or No

COMPLETE SENTENCES
Answer

2

No

COMPLETE SENTENCES
Question

3

Is the sentence a complete sentence?

Marrin goes to kindergarten.

Yes or No

COMPLETE SENTENCES
Answer

3

Yes

Cooperative Learning & Grammar
Kagan Publishing • 1 (800) 933-2667 • www.KaganOnline.com

Instructions: Cut out each card along the dotted line. Then fold each card in half so the question is on one side and the answer is on the back. Glue or tape the cards together to keep the answers and questions on opposite sides.

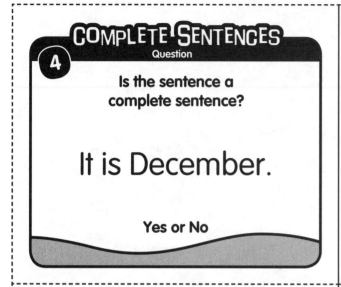

COMPLETE SENTENCES
Question

4

Is the sentence a complete sentence?

It is December.

Yes or No

COMPLETE SENTENCES
Answer

4

Yes

COMPLETE SENTENCES
Question

5

Is the sentence a complete sentence?

Can you sing the song again?

Yes or No

COMPLETE SENTENCES
Answer

5

Yes

COMPLETE SENTENCES
Question

6

Is the sentence a complete sentence?

Dog barking loudly.

Yes or No

COMPLETE SENTENCES
Answer

6

No

COMPLETE SENTENCES
Quiz-Quiz-Trade

Instructions: Cut out each card along the dotted line. Then fold each card in half so the question is on one side and the answer is on the back. Glue or tape the cards together to keep the answers and questions on opposite sides.

COMPLETE SENTENCES
Question

7

Is the sentence a complete sentence?

The birds chirp in the field.

Yes or No

COMPLETE SENTENCES
Answer

7

Yes

COMPLETE SENTENCES
Question

8

Is the sentence a complete sentence?

The duck.

Yes or No

COMPLETE SENTENCES
Answer

8

No

COMPLETE SENTENCES
Question

9

Is the sentence a complete sentence?

Megan asked me to play.

Yes or No

COMPLETE SENTENCES
Answer

9

Yes

Cooperative Learning & Grammar
Kagan Publishing • 1 (800) 933-2667 • www.KaganOnline.com

COMPLETE SENTENCES
Quiz-Quiz-Trade

Instructions: Cut out each card along the dotted line. Then fold each card in half so the question is on one side and the answer is on the back. Glue or tape the cards together to keep the answers and questions on opposite sides.

COMPLETE SENTENCES
Question

10

Is the sentence a complete sentence?

Ms. Hackman gave us spelling words.

Yes or No

COMPLETE SENTENCES
Answer

10

Yes

COMPLETE SENTENCES
Question

11

Is the sentence a complete sentence?

In the classroom.

Yes or No

COMPLETE SENTENCES
Answer

11

No

COMPLETE SENTENCES
Question

12

Is the sentence a complete sentence?

I play.

Yes or No

COMPLETE SENTENCES
Answer

12

Yes

COMPLETE SENTENCES
Quiz-Quiz-Trade

Instructions: Cut out each card along the dotted line. Then fold each card in half so the question is on one side and the answer is on the back. Glue or tape the cards together to keep the answers and questions on opposite sides.

COMPLETE SENTENCES
Question

13

Is the sentence a complete sentence?

Najem's favorite book is *Curious George®.*

Yes or No

COMPLETE SENTENCES
Answer

13

Yes

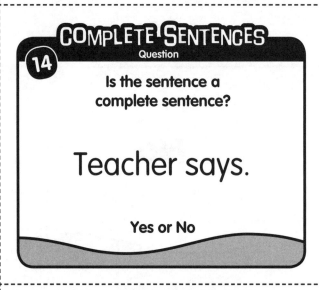

COMPLETE SENTENCES
Question

14

Is the sentence a complete sentence?

Teacher says.

Yes or No

COMPLETE SENTENCES
Answer

14

No

COMPLETE SENTENCES
Question

15

Is the sentence a complete sentence?

I go?

Yes or No

COMPLETE SENTENCES
Answer

15

No

Cooperative Learning & Grammar
Kagan Publishing • 1 (800) 933-2667 • www.KaganOnline.com

COMPLETE SENTENCES
Quiz-Quiz-Trade

Instructions: Cut out each card along the dotted line. Then fold each card in half so the question is on one side and the answer is on the back. Glue or tape the cards together to keep the answers and questions on opposite sides.

COMPLETE SENTENCES
Question

16

Is the sentence a complete sentence?

I cold outside.

Yes or No

COMPLETE SENTENCES
Answer

16

No

COMPLETE SENTENCES
Question

17

Is the sentence a complete sentence?

I am a big sister.

Yes or No

COMPLETE SENTENCES
Answer

17

Yes

COMPLETE SENTENCES
Question

18

Is the sentence a complete sentence?

The cat likes to cuddle.

Yes or No

COMPLETE SENTENCES
Answer

18

Yes

COMPLETE SENTENCES
Quiz-Quiz-Trade

Instructions: Cut out each card along the dotted line. Then fold each card in half so the question is on one side and the answer is on the back. Glue or tape the cards together to keep the answers and questions on opposite sides.

COMPLETE SENTENCES
19
Question

Is the sentence a
complete sentence?

Under the bridge.

Yes or No

COMPLETE SENTENCES
19
Answer

No

COMPLETE SENTENCES
20
Question

Is the sentence a
complete sentence?

Sledding down
the hill.

Yes or No

COMPLETE SENTENCES
20
Answer

No

COMPLETE SENTENCES
21
Question

Is the sentence a
complete sentence?

Kirby makes toys.

Yes or No

COMPLETE SENTENCES
21
Answer

Yes

Cooperative Learning & Grammar
Kagan Publishing • 1 (800) 933-2667 • www.KaganOnline.com

COMPLETE SENTENCES
Quiz-Quiz-Trade

Instructions: Cut out each card along the dotted line. Then fold each card in half so the question is on one side and the answer is on the back. Glue or tape the cards together to keep the answers and questions on opposite sides.

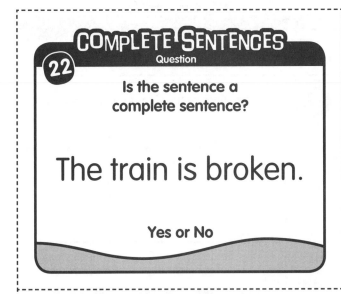

COMPLETE SENTENCES
Question

22

Is the sentence a complete sentence?

The train is broken.

Yes or No

COMPLETE SENTENCES
Answer

22

Yes

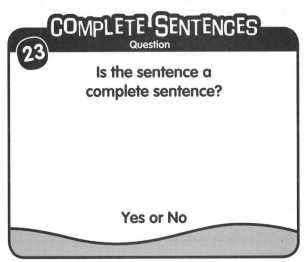

COMPLETE SENTENCES
Question

23

Is the sentence a complete sentence?

Yes or No

COMPLETE SENTENCES
Answer

23

COMPLETE SENTENCES
Question

24

Is the sentence a complete sentence?

Yes or No

COMPLETE SENTENCES
Answer

24

SENTENCE WORD ORDER
RallyCoach/Sage-N-Scribe

Instructions: Take turns with your partner rearranging the words below to form a complete sentence. Write the sentence on the lines. Use RallyCoach or Sage-N-Scribe to rewrite the sentence.

PARTNER A	PARTNER B
Name	Name

1 growing tree tall. really The is

1 you again? read Can book this me to

2 fetch. dog is play wanting My to

2 begin play The hour. will one in

3 go is school. time to It to

3 blanket. wants baby The his

4 pig the in The mud. is rolling

4 is lunch. to eat It time

Cooperative Learning & Grammar
Kagan Publishing • 1 (800) 933-2667 • www.KaganOnline.com

Instructions: Pair up and take turns rearranging the words to make a complete sentence below. Don't forget to get your partner's initials.

	Sentence Words	Complete Sentence	Initials
1	bed. hiding The under is the dog	_____ _____ _____	
2	birthday. wants for a her Sloan doll	_____ _____ _____	
3	down rabbit The street. hops the	_____ _____ _____	
4	lost park. his the teddy bear Billy at	_____ _____ _____	
5	Mrs. book. us read Glenn a	_____ _____ _____	
6	I mail. a in got the letter	_____ _____	

SENTENCE WORD ORDER
Fan-N-Pick/Showdown

Instructions: Copy one set of cards for each team. Cut out each card along the dotted line. Give each team a set of cards to play Fan-N-Pick or Showdown.

SENTENCE WORD ORDER

1 Arrange the words in order so they make sense.

broke computer today The.

_____

SENTENCE WORD ORDER

2 Arrange the words in order so they make sense.

dog a fence jumped The.

_____

SENTENCE WORD ORDER

3 Arrange the words in order so they make sense.

stain had rug The a.

_____

SENTENCE WORD ORDER

4 Arrange the words in order so they make sense.

movie a watch Can we?

_____

SENTENCE WORD ORDER

5 Arrange the words in order so they make sense.

mom My drives a car blue.

_____

SENTENCE WORD ORDER

6 Arrange the words in order so they make sense.

grass The ate the cow.

_____

Cooperative Learning & Grammar
Kagan Publishing • 1 (800) 933-2667 • www.KaganOnline.com

Instructions: Copy one set of cards for each team. Cut out each card along the dotted line. Give each team a set of cards to play Fan-N-Pick or Showdown.

SENTENCE WORD ORDER

7 Arrange the words in order so they make sense.

Johnny come When home does?

_____

SENTENCE WORD ORDER

8 Arrange the words in order so they make sense.

enjoys pizza hamburger Kolby.

_____

SENTENCE WORD ORDER

9 Arrange the words in order so they make sense.

won race Lucy the.

_____

SENTENCE WORD ORDER

10 Arrange the words in order so they make sense.

pond The frozen was.

_____

SENTENCE WORD ORDER

11 Arrange the words in order so they make sense.

games Mario video likes.

_____

SENTENCE WORD ORDER

12 Arrange the words in order so they make sense.

fly Ducks south winter for the.

_____

Types of Sentences: Statements
RallyCoach/Sage-N-Scribe

KEY IDEA Statements share **facts, opinions, or ideas**. This is the most common type of sentence. It always ends in a period (.).

Example: The turtle swims in the ocean.

Instructions: Take turns working with your partner to identify the sentence as either a statement or not a statement. Circle the correct answer. Use RallyCoach or Sage-N-Scribe to solve the problem.

Partner A

Name _____

1 Wyatt likes to read books.

Statement   Not Statement

2 Watch out for that car!

Statement   Not Statement

3 Can you please hand me my pencil?

Statement   Not Statement

4 The computer is on the shelf.

Statement   Not Statement

5 The flowers are ready to bloom in spring.

Statement   Not Statement

Partner B

Name _____

1 When is your birthday?

Statement   Not Statement

2 The milk is in the refrigerator.

Statement   Not Statement

3 The princess lives in a castle.

Statement   Not Statement

4 Do not touch the stove!

Statement   Not Statement

5 Where do you go to school?

Statement   Not Statement

Cooperative Learning & Grammar
Kagan Publishing • 1 (800) 933-2667 • www.KaganOnline.com

KEY IDEA

Statements share **facts, opinions, or ideas**. This is the most common type of sentence. It always ends in a period (.).

Example: The turtle swims in the ocean.

Instructions: Take turns working with your partner writing each statement so it has a capital letter and a period. Use RallyCoach or Sage-N-Scribe to solve the problem.

PARTNER A

Name _____

1 it is really raining outside

_____

_____

_____

2 i love to eat apples for lunch

_____

_____

_____

3 we are going to swim at the pool

_____

_____

_____

PARTNER B

Name _____

1 grandaddy is coming to visit

_____

_____

_____

2 the car needs more gas

_____

_____

_____

3 the balloons are popping

_____

_____

_____

TYPES OF SENTENCES: QUESTIONS
RallyCoach/Sage-N-Scribe

KEY IDEA
Question sentences **ask** to find out information. All question sentences end in a question mark (?).

Example: What is your favorite color?

Instructions: Take turns working with your partner to identify the sentence as either a question or not a question. Circle the correct answer. Use RallyCoach or Sage-N-Scribe to solve the problem.

PARTNER A

Name _____

1 Where is my backpack?

(Question)   (Not Question)

2 My favorite animal is a bear.

(Question)   (Not Question)

3 Have you seen my pencil?

(Question)   (Not Question)

4 Jarrod is coming over to play.

(Question)   (Not Question)

5 When can I go to the park?

(Question)   (Not Question)

PARTNER B

Name _____

1 How old are you today?

(Question)   (Not Question)

2 Can you a read a book to me?

(Question)   (Not Question)

3 I want to be a firefighter when I get older.

(Question)   (Not Question)

4 The cat is hiding under the bed.

(Question)   (Not Question)

5 How do you make a peanut butter sandwich?

(Question)   (Not Question)

Cooperative Learning & Grammar
Kagan Publishing • 1 (800) 933-2667 • www.KaganOnline.com

TYPES OF SENTENCES: QUESTIONS
RallyCoach/Sage-N-Scribe

KEY IDEA

Question sentences **ask** to find out information. All question sentences end in a question mark (?).

Example: What is your favorite color?

Instructions: Take turns with your partner rewriting each question so it has a capital letter and a question mark. Use RallyCoach or Sage-N-Scribe to solve the problem.

PARTNER A	PARTNER B
Name _____	Name _____
1 where are my shoes	**1** can I have pizza for dinner
2 what is for lunch	**2** how do I zip my coat
3 why are the pigs in the mud	**3** did you read this book

TYPES OF SENTENCES: EXCLAMATIONS
RallyCoach/Sage-N-Scribe

Instructions: Take turns working with your partner to identify the sentence as either an exclamation or not an exclamation. Circle the correct answer. Use RallyCoach or Sage-N-Scribe to solve the problem.

PARTNER A

Name _____

1 My favorite color is purple.

Exclamation | Not Exclamation

2 That movie was scary!

Exclamation | Not Exclamation

3 Rachel is my best friend!

Exclamation | Not Exclamation

4 Najem is going to be 3 today!

Exclamation | Not Exclamation

5 The rug is very dirty.

Exclamation | Not Exclamation

PARTNER B

Name _____

1 Please put away the DVDs.

Exclamation | Not Exclamation

2 What are you going to read this summer?

Exclamation | Not Exclamation

3 I love dance!

Exclamation | Not Exclamation

4 I hurt my arm falling out of the tree!

Exclamation | Not Exclamation

5 I just got a present for my birthday!

Exclamation | Not Exclamation

# TYPES OF SENTENCES: EXCLAMATIONS
RallyCoach/Sage-N-Scribe

KEY IDEA — Exclamation sentences **show** excitement or strong feeling. All exclamation sentences end with an exclamation mark (!).

Example: That was fun!

Instructions: Take turns working with your partner writing each exclamation sentence so it has a capital letter and an exclamation mark. Use RallyCoach or Sage-N-Scribe to solve the problem.

PARTNER A

Name _____

1 i am laughing too hard

_____

_____

_____

2 help

_____

_____

_____

3 we won the race

_____

_____

_____

PARTNER B

Name _____

1 I can't wait to see my grandma

_____

_____

_____

2 that ride was fast

_____

_____

_____

3 i see a frog

_____

_____

_____

Types of Sentences: Commands
RallyCoach/Sage-N-Scribe

KEY IDEA

Commands are **telling** someone to do something. Commands can end with a period (.) or an exclamation point (!) if there is feeling with the command.

Examples: Wash your dishes.   or   Watch out for that car!

Instructions: Take turns working with your partner to identify the sentence as either a command or not a command. Circle the correct answer. Use RallyCoach or Sage-N-Scribe to solve the problem.

PARTNER A

Name _____

1 Please read quietly.

Command   **Not Command**

2 The toy train is very quiet.

Command   **Not Command**

3 Don't pull my hair!

Command   **Not Command**

4 It is so much fun to ski!

Command   **Not Command**

5 Where is my favorite sweatshirt?

Command   **Not Command**

PARTNER B

Name _____

1 Go put away the laundry in the drawers.

Command   **Not Command**

2 Brush your teeth before you go to bed.

Command   **Not Command**

3 Kolby needs to make his bed.

Command   **Not Command**

4 Please do not scream in the library.

Command   **Not Command**

5 The piano keys are all broken.

Command   **Not Command**

Cooperative Learning & Grammar
Kagan Publishing • 1 (800) 933-2667 • www.KaganOnline.com

KEY IDEA Commands are **telling** someone to do something. Commands can end with a period (.) or an exclamation point (!) if there is feeling with the command.

Examples: Wash your dishes.   or   Watch out for that car!

Instructions: Take turns working with your partner writing each command so it has a capital letter and a period or an exclamation point. Use RallyCoach or Sage-N-Scribe to solve the problem.

PARTNER A	PARTNER B
Name _____	Name _____
1 clean your room	**1** please dust the shelves
2 do not touch the stove	**2** put on your coat
3 turn off the computer	**3** watch your step

KEY IDEAS

Telling sentences **tell** you something and always end with a period (.).
Asking sentences **ask** for information and always end in a question mark (?).

Examples: Tell: I have a cat named Smokey.
Ask: What is your favorite movie?

Instructions: Take turns working with your partner to identify the sentence as either a telling sentence or an asking sentence. Circle the correct answer. Use RallyCoach or Sage-N-Scribe to solve the problem.

PARTNER A

Name _____

1 I brushed my hair.

Telling   Asking

2 The dog is barking.

Telling   Asking

3 What is your phone number?

Telling   Asking

4 What time is it now?

Telling   Asking

5 My name is Marrin.

Telling   Asking

PARTNER A

Name _____

1 Are we there yet?

Telling   Asking

2 Mom baked cookies.

Telling   Asking

3 Do you think it will snow?

Telling   Asking

4 Can I call my dad?

Telling   Asking

5 I love to sing and dance.

Telling   Asking

Cooperative Learning & Grammar
Kagan Publishing • 1 (800) 933-2667 • www.KaganOnline.com

Instructions: Pair up and take turns identifying if the sentence is a question, command, or statement. Don't forget to get your partner's initials.

1 Get out your pencils.

_____ Initials

2 Who is wearing red?

_____ Initials

3 Clean up your room.

_____ Initials

4 What time is lunch?

_____ Initials

5 I like cheese pizza.

_____ Initials

6 Your new sweater is pretty.

_____ Initials

7 Move to another seat.

_____ Initials

8 Where is your coat?

_____ Initials

9 Thank you for being helpful.

_____ Initials

command

ASKING OR TELLING SENTENCES
Find Someone Who

Name _____

Instructions: Pair up and take turns identifying if the sentence is asking or telling. Circle the correct answer. Don't forget to get your partner's initials.

Sentence	Asking or Telling	Initials
1 I like pizza.	(Asking) (Telling)	
2 Where are you going?	(Asking) (Telling)	
3 My birthday is on Friday.	(Asking) (Telling)	
4 Bill went running.	(Asking) (Telling)	
5 What is your name?	(Asking) (Telling)	
6 Can you go camping?	(Asking) (Telling)	
7 My mom has red hair.	(Asking) (Telling)	
8 Where is the lake?	(Asking) (Telling)	
9 Does Sarah have new glasses?	(Asking) (Telling)	

Cooperative Learning & Grammar
Kagan Publishing • 1 (800) 933-2667 • www.KaganOnline.com

SENTENCE·TYPES
Fan-N-Pick/Showdown

Instructions: Copy one set of cards for each team. Cut out each card along the dotted line. Give each team a set of cards to play Fan-N-Pick or Showdown.

SENTENCE·TYPES

1 Rewrite the sentence to include a capital letter and punctuation. Then tell if it is a command, question, or statement.

lucy lost her pink ring

SENTENCE·TYPES

2 Rewrite the sentence to include a capital letter and punctuation. Then tell if it is a command, question, or statement.

the campfire was hot

SENTENCE·TYPES

3 Rewrite the sentence to include a capital letter and punctuation. Then tell if it is a command, question, or statement.

will you be at the party

SENTENCE·TYPES

4 Rewrite the sentence to include a capital letter and punctuation. Then tell if it is a command, question, or statement.

today's fire alarm was noisy

SENTENCE·TYPES

5 Rewrite the sentence to include a capital letter and punctuation. Then tell if it is a command, question, or statement.

five birds sat on a branch

SENTENCE·TYPES

6 Rewrite the sentence to include a capital letter and punctuation. Then tell if it is a command, question, or statement.

get out your pencils

Instructions: Copy one set of cards for each team. Cut out each card along the dotted line. Give each team a set of cards to play Fan-N-Pick or Showdown.

SENTENCE·TYPES

7 Rewrite the sentence to include a capital letter and punctuation. Then tell if it is a command, question, or statement.

did you find your coat

SENTENCE·TYPES

8 Rewrite the sentence to include a capital letter and punctuation. Then tell if it is a command, question, or statement.

turn to page 45 in your math book

SENTENCE·TYPES

9 Rewrite the sentence to include a capital letter and punctuation. Then tell if it is a command, question, or statement.

do your homework before dinner

SENTENCE·TYPES

10 Rewrite the sentence to include a capital letter and punctuation. Then tell if it is a command, question, or statement.

what is your last name

SENTENCE·TYPES

11 Rewrite the sentence to include a capital letter and punctuation. Then tell if it is a command, question, or statement.

the shirt was too big

SENTENCE·TYPES

12 Rewrite the sentence to include a capital letter and punctuation. Then tell if it is a command, question, or statement.

soccer is my favorite sport

KEY IDEAS

A sentence has two parts, the naming part and the action part. The **naming part** tells who or what the sentence is about. The **action part** of a sentence tells what the naming part is doing or did.

Examples: <u>The ball</u> bounced down the street. (naming part)
Lucy <u>rides her bike</u>. (action part)

Instructions: In the sentences below, underline the naming part of each sentence and circle the action part. Take turns working with your partner to solve the problems using RallyCoach or Sage-N-Scribe.

PARTNER A

Name _____

1 Our class took a field trip to the zoo.

2 The elephants moved slowly.

3 The popcorn was good to eat.

4 The bus driver drove us back to school.

5 My mom bought me an ice cream.

6 Some teachers petted the giraffe.

PARTNER B

Name _____

1 The kids feed the goats at the petting zoo.

2 Big trees grew in the lion den.

3 A man was feeding the tigers.

4 A big wind blew the leaves.

5 Rain fell from the sky.

6 Everyone ran to the bus.

Instructions: Pair up and take turns underlining the naming part of the sentence. Don't forget to get your partner's initials.

Initials

1 Josh ran down the street.

2 Gabe and Beth had a picnic.

3 They fed bread to the ducks.

4 The basket tipped over in the wind.

5 The round apple was juicy.

6 The playground was crowded.

7 John took pictures of the lake.

8 The blanket got dirty.

9 The ducks ate the bread.

Cooperative Learning & Grammar
Kagan Publishing • 1 (800) 933-2667 • www.KaganOnline.com

WRITING THE ACTION PART
RallyCoach/Sage-N-Scribe

KEY IDEA: The action part of a sentence tells what the naming part is doing or did.

Example: Lucy <u>rides her bike</u>.

Instructions: Take turns working with your partner identifying the action parts in the box that best completes each sentence below. Write the action part on the lines. Use RallyCoach or Sage-N-Scribe to solve the problem.

PARTNER A

Name _____

| sat on the shelf | smelled like food |
| blew the whistle | broke into pieces |

1 The teacher _____

_____

_____ .

2 The crayons _____

_____

_____ .

3 The books _____

_____

_____ .

4 The lunchroom _____

_____

_____ .

PARTNER A

Name _____

| rang three times | swam in the bowl |
| spilled on the floor | played at recess |

1 Our class pet _____

_____

_____ .

2 The bell _____

_____

_____ .

3 Juice _____

_____

_____ .

4 The kids _____

_____

_____ .

ACTION PART
Fan-N-Pick/Showdown

Instructions: Copy one set of cards for each team. Cut out each card along the dotted line. Give each team a set of cards to play Fan-N-Pick or Showdown.

ACTION PART

1 Which action part matches the naming part?

The fireman _____

a. rescued the little girl.
b. built a tree house.
c. painted a picture.

ACTION PART

2 Which action part matches the naming part?

My cat _____

a. hopped away.
b. liked his hoof.
c. climbed a tree.

ACTION PART

3 Which action part matches the naming part?

The doctor _____

a. delivered the mail.
b. helped the sick boy.
c. hopped into the lake.

ACTION PART

4 Which action part matches the naming part?

The goldfish _____

a. swam in circles.
b. jumped off the swing.
c. went for a walk.

ACTION PART

5 Which action part matches the naming part?

The beautiful flower _____

a. climbed up a tree.
b. ran down the street.
c. grew tall.

ACTION PART

6 Which action part matches the naming part?

The little boy _____

a. flapped his wings.
b. drew a picture.
c. ate his dog food.

Cooperative Learning & Grammar
Kagan Publishing • 1 (800) 933-2667 • www.KaganOnline.com

Action Part
Fan-N-Pick/Showdown

Instructions: Copy one set of cards for each team. Cut out each card along the dotted line. Give each team a set of cards to play Fan-N-Pick or Showdown.

ACTION PART

7 Which action part matches the naming part?

The mailman _____

a. chased his tail.
b. flew south for the winter.
c. delivered the package.

ACTION PART

8 Which action part matches the naming part?

The blue bird _____

a. washed the dishes.
b. flew into the tree.
c. jogged around the lake.

ACTION PART

9 Which action part matches the naming part?

The frog _____

a. ate a fly.
b. climbed a cheeseburger.
c. washed the car.

ACTION PART

10 Which action part matches the naming part?

The house _____

a. was painted blue.
b. kicked the ball.
c. hit the homerun.

ACTION PART

11 Which action part matches the naming part?

The large bear _____

a. read a book.
b. got an A on his test.
c. ran into the woods.

ACTION PART

12 Which action part matches the naming part?

The tall, green tree _____

a. looked in the mirror.
b. was chopped down.
c. lost his mother.

Action Part
Fan-N-Pick/Showdown

Instructions: Copy one set of cards for each team. Cut out each card along the dotted line. Give each team a set of cards to play Fan-N-Pick or Showdown.

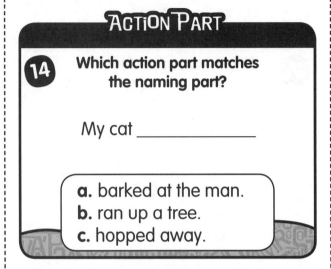

ACTION PART

13 Which action part matches the naming part?

The baby _____

a. made the bed.
b. cried all night.
c. went to work.

ACTION PART

14 Which action part matches the naming part?

My cat _____

a. barked at the man.
b. ran up a tree.
c. hopped away.

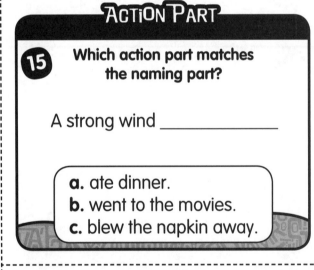

ACTION PART

15 Which action part matches the naming part?

A strong wind _____

a. ate dinner.
b. went to the movies.
c. blew the napkin away.

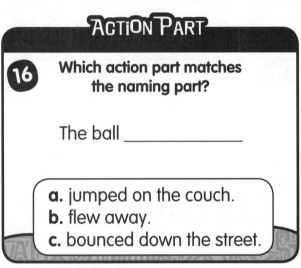

ACTION PART

16 Which action part matches the naming part?

The ball _____

a. jumped on the couch.
b. flew away.
c. bounced down the street.

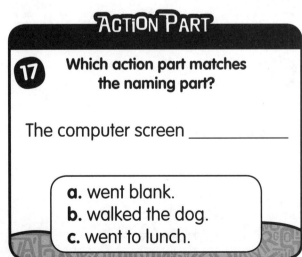

ACTION PART

17 Which action part matches the naming part?

The computer screen _____

a. went blank.
b. walked the dog.
c. went to lunch.

ACTION PART

18 Which action part matches the naming part?

The drums _____

a. were loud.
b. painted a picture.
c. played outside.

Cooperative Learning & Grammar
Kagan Publishing • 1 (800) 933-2667 • www.KaganOnline.com

NAMING & ACTION PARTS OF A SENTENCE
Fan-N-Pick/Showdown

Instructions: Copy one set of cards for each team. Cut out each card along the dotted line. Give each team a set of cards to play Fan-N-Pick or Showdown.

NAMING & ACTION PARTS OF A SENTENCE

1 Which naming part best completes the sentence?

_____ made fresh bread.

a. The dog
b. The pencil
c. The baker

NAMING & ACTION PARTS OF A SENTENCE

2 Which action part best completes the sentence?

The nice lady _____

a. ran up a tree.
b. cooked dinner.
c. started to pour.

NAMING & ACTION PARTS OF A SENTENCE

3 Which naming part best completes the sentence?

_____ blew the napkin.

a. A strong cat
b. A strong wind
c. A strong table

NAMING & ACTION PARTS OF A SENTENCE

4 Which action part best completes the sentence?

The mittens _____

a. drove away.
b. wrote a story.
c. got lost.

NAMING & ACTION PARTS OF A SENTENCE

5 Which naming part best completes the sentence?

_____ barked loudly.

a. The dog
b. The pencil
c. The baker

NAMING & ACTION PARTS OF A SENTENCE

6 Which action part best completes the sentence?

The bed _____

a. had two pillows.
b. walked to the park.
c. acted in the play.

Instructions: Copy one set of cards for each team. Cut out each card along the dotted line. Give each team a set of cards to play Fan-N-Pick or Showdown.

NAMING & ACTION PARTS OF A SENTENCE

7 Which naming part best completes the sentence?

_____ gets a capital letter.

a. Each sentence
b. The pencil
c. Mom

NAMING & ACTION PARTS OF A SENTENCE

8 Which action part best completes the sentence?

_____ painted a picture.

a. The elephant
b. The artist
c. The door

NAMING & ACTION PARTS OF A SENTENCE

9 Which naming part best completes the sentence?

_____ keep your toes warm.

a. Mittens
b. Hats
c. Socks

NAMING & ACTION PARTS OF A SENTENCE

10 Which action part best completes the sentence?

_____ has five drawers.

a. The fishbowl
b. The shower
c. The dresser

NAMING & ACTION PARTS OF A SENTENCE

11 Which naming part best completes the sentence?

_____ slammed loudly.

a. The door
b. The frog
c. The lake

NAMING & ACTION PARTS OF A SENTENCE

12 Which action part best completes the sentence?

_____ sing loudly in the morning.

a. Cats
b. Sinks
c. Birds

Cooperative Learning & Grammar
Kagan Publishing • 1 (800) 933-2667 • www.KaganOnline.com

Grammar Skills 5

WORKING WITH WORDS

Spelling

ABC ORDER
RallyCoach/Sage-N-Scribe

Instructions: Underline the first letter in each word. Then write the words in ABC order. Take turns working with your partner to solve the problems using RallyCoach or Sage-N-Scribe.

PARTNER A

Name _____

1

Ring

Necklace

ABC _____ _____

2

Cake

Apple

ABC _____ _____

3

Hat

Shoe

ABC _____ _____

PARTNER B

Name _____

1

Car

Truck

ABC _____ _____

2

Guitar

Drum

ABC _____ _____

3

Eye

Tooth

ABC _____ _____

Cooperative Learning & Grammar
Kagan Publishing • 1 (800) 933-2667 • www.KaganOnline.com

ABC ORDER
Find-N-Fix

Name _____

Instructions: For each problem, find the words in the incorrect order. Indicate which is incorrect using your Find-N-Fix cards. When your team agrees, write the words in the box in alphabetical order.

---

1 **Which of the following is NOT in alphabetical order?**

a. dog, duck, girl

b. bike, bump, broom

c. apple, banana, orange

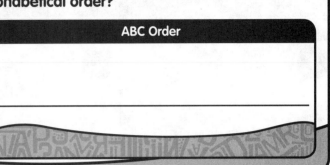

ABC Order

---

2 **Which of the following is NOT in alphabetical order?**

a. lake, long, love

b. boy, mom, dad

c. golf, grass, green

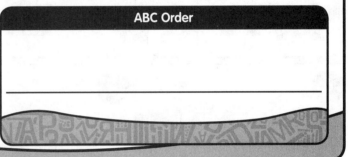

ABC Order

---

3 **Which of the following is NOT in alphabetical order?**

a. balloon, dog, elephant

b. wait, watch, while

c. desk, door, damp

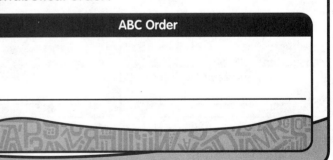

ABC Order

---

4 **Which of the following is NOT in alphabetical order?**

a. said, say, sail

b. cent, scent, small

c. my, she, they

ABC Order

Name _____

Instructions: Pair up and take turns writing the missing letter in the space. Don't forget to get your partner's initials.

1

A B C D __ F G

Initials

2

L M N O __

Initials

3

s t __ v w x

Initials

4

j k l __ n o

Initials

5

E F G __ I J

Initials

6

i __ k l m n

Initials

7

c __ e f g h __

Initials

8

N O P __ R S __

Initials

9

V __ X Y Z

Initials

Cooperative Learning & Grammar
Kagan Publishing • 1 (800) 933-2667 • www.KaganOnline.com

Name _____

Instructions: Pair up and take turns circling the word that comes first in ABC order. Don't forget to get your partner's initials.

1	2	3
Milk	Computer	Apple
Cheese	Book	Watermelon
Bread	Pencil	Cantaloupe
Initials	Initials	Initials

4	5	6
Couch	Sunglasses	Brush
Table	Jeans	Ribbon
Chair	Boots	Comb
Initials	Initials	Initials

7	8	9
Title	Missouri	House
Glossary	Alaska	School
Index	California	Church
Initials	Initials	Initials

WRITING ABC ORDER
Fan-N-Pick/Showdown

Instructions: Copy one set of cards for each team. Cut out each card along the dotted line. Give each team a set of cards to play Fan-N-Pick or Showdown.

WRITING ABC ORDER

1

Write the words in ABC order.

say, all, must

WRITING ABC ORDER

2

Write the words in ABC order.

kite, boy, sand

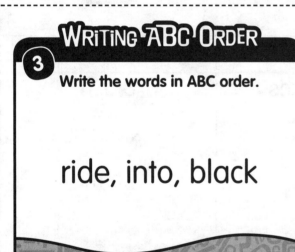

WRITING ABC ORDER

3

Write the words in ABC order.

ride, into, black

WRITING ABC ORDER

4

Write the words in ABC order.

pretty, eat, four

WRITING ABC ORDER

5

Write the words in ABC order.

new, have, be

WRITING ABC ORDER

6

Write the words in ABC order.

ran, have, am

Cooperative Learning & Grammar
Kagan Publishing • 1 (800) 933-2667 • www.KaganOnline.com

WRITING ABC ORDER
Fan-N-Pick/Showdown

Instructions: Copy one set of cards for each team. Cut out each card along the dotted line. Give each team a set of cards to play Fan-N-Pick or Showdown.

WRITING ABC ORDER

7 Write the words in ABC order.

me, two, cat, red

WRITING ABC ORDER

8 Write the words in ABC order.

did, out, are, there

WRITING ABC ORDER

9 Write the words in ABC order.

one, fun, it, blue

WRITING ABC ORDER

10 Write the words in ABC order.

who, she, our, with

WRITING ABC ORDER

11 Write the words in ABC order.

come, play, go, and

WRITING ABC ORDER

12 Write the words in ABC order.

like, the, can, no

Instructions: Copy one set of cards for each team. Cut out each card along the dotted line. Give each team a set of cards to play Fan-N-Pick or Showdown.

WRITING ABC ORDER

13

Write the words in ABC order.

going, came, am, here

WRITING ABC ORDER

14

Write the words in ABC order.

my, said, will, has

WRITING ABC ORDER

15

Write the words in ABC order.

went, good, as, your

WRITING ABC ORDER

16

Write the words in ABC order.

three, green, we, off

WRITING ABC ORDER

17

Write the words in ABC order.

stop, brown, top, big

WRITING ABC ORDER

18

Write the words in ABC order.

black, six, white, sit

Cooperative Learning & Grammar
Kagan Publishing • 1 (800) 933-2667 • www.KaganOnline.com

ABC ORDER
Fan-N-Pick/Showdown

Instructions: Copy one set of cards for each team. Cut out each card along the dotted line. Give each team a set of cards to play Fan-N-Pick or Showdown.

ABC ORDER

1 Which group of words is in ABC order?

a. table, bed, desk

b. desk, bed, table

c. bed, desk, table

ABC ORDER

2 Which group of words is in ABC order?

a. dog, dad, mom

b. mom, dad, dog

c. dad, dog, mom

ABC ORDER

3 Which group of words is in ABC order?

a. pear, peach, banana

b. banana, peach, pear

c. peach, banana, pear

ABC ORDER

4 Which group of words is in ABC order?

a. moon, star, sky

b. moon, sky, star

c. sky, star, moon

ABC ORDER

5 Which group of words is in ABC order?

a. ring, finger, nail

b. finger, nail, ring

c. nail, finger, ring

ABC ORDER

6 Which group of words is in ABC order?

a. airplane, bike, truck

b. bike, truck, airplane

c. truck, bike, airplane

Instructions: Copy one set of cards for each team. Cut out each card along the dotted line. Give each team a set of cards to play Fan-N-Pick or Showdown.

ABC ORDER

7

Which group of words is in ABC order?

a. cat, dog, mouse

b. dog, cat, mouse

c. dog, mouse, cat

ABC ORDER

8

Which group of words is in ABC order?

a. door, floor, rug

b. floor, door, rug

c. rug, floor, door

ABC ORDER

9

Which group of words is in ABC order?

a. Wednesday, Friday, Monday

b. Friday, Wednesday, Monday

c. Friday, Monday, Wednesday

ABC ORDER

10

Which group of words is in ABC order?

a. purple, blue, yellow

b. yellow, blue, purple

c. blue, purple, yellow

ABC ORDER

11

Which group of words is in ABC order?

a. ball, bat, glove

b. bat, ball, glove

c. glove, ball, bat

ABC ORDER

12

Which group of words is in ABC order?

a. play, jump, run

b. jump, run, play

c. jump, play, run

Cooperative Learning & Grammar
Kagan Publishing • 1 (800) 933-2667 • www.KaganOnline.com

Instructions: Copy one set of cards for each team. Cut out each card along the dotted line. Give each team a set of cards to play Fan-N-Pick or Showdown.

ABC ORDER

13 Which group of words is in ABC order?

a. pretty, kind, smart

b. kind, smart, pretty

c. kind, pretty, smart

ABC ORDER

14 Which group of words is in ABC order?

a. cup, glass, plate

b. glass, cup, plate

c. plate, cup, glass

ABC ORDER

15 Which group of words is in ABC order?

a. brush, basket, broom

b. broom, brush, basket

c. basket, broom, brush

ABC ORDER

16 Which group of words is in ABC order?

a. water, soap, bath

b. bath, water, soap

c. bath, soap, water

ABC ORDER

17 Which group of words is in ABC order?

a. baby, boy, girl

b. boy, girl, baby

c. girl, boy, baby

ABC ORDER

18 Which group of words is in ABC order?

a. sand, bucket, towel

b. bucket, sand, towel

c. sand, towel, bucket

ABC Order
Quiz-Quiz-Trade

Instructions: Cut out each card along the dotted line. Then fold each card in half so the question is on one side and the answer is on the back. Glue or tape the cards together to keep the answers and questions on opposite sides.

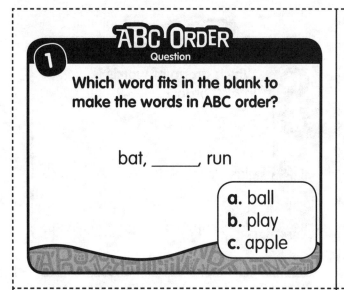

ABC ORDER
Question

1

Which word fits in the blank to make the words in ABC order?

bat, _____, run

a. ball
b. play
c. apple

ABC ORDER
Answer

1

b. play

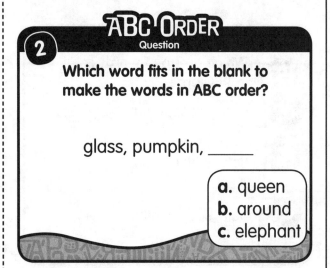

ABC ORDER
Question

2

Which word fits in the blank to make the words in ABC order?

glass, pumpkin, _____

a. queen
b. around
c. elephant

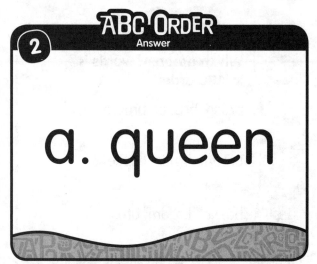

ABC ORDER
Answer

2

a. queen

ABC ORDER
Question

3

Which word fits in the blank to make the words in ABC order?

_____, me, you

a. us
b. they
c. he

ABC ORDER
Answer

3

c. he

Cooperative Learning & Grammar
Kagan Publishing • 1 (800) 933-2667 • www.KaganOnline.com

Instructions: Cut out each card along the dotted line. Then fold each card in half so the question is on one side and the answer is on the back. Glue or tape the cards together to keep the answers and questions on opposite sides.

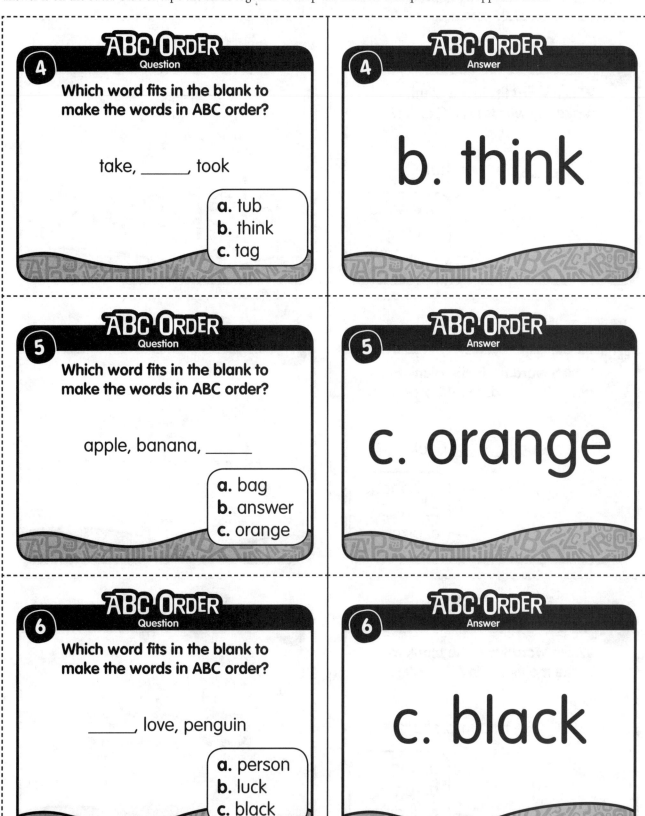

ABC ORDER
Question

4

Which word fits in the blank to make the words in ABC order?

take, _____, took

a. tub
b. think
c. tag

ABC ORDER
Answer

4

b. think

ABC ORDER
Question

5

Which word fits in the blank to make the words in ABC order?

apple, banana, _____

a. bag
b. answer
c. orange

ABC ORDER
Answer

5

c. orange

ABC ORDER
Question

6

Which word fits in the blank to make the words in ABC order?

_____, love, penguin

a. person
b. luck
c. black

ABC ORDER
Answer

6

c. black

Instructions: Cut out each card along the dotted line. Then fold each card in half so the question is on one side and the answer is on the back. Glue or tape the cards together to keep the answers and questions on opposite sides.

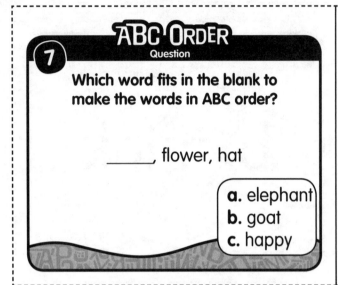

ABC Order
Question

7

Which word fits in the blank to make the words in ABC order?

_____, flower, hat

a. elephant
b. goat
c. happy

ABC Order
Answer

7

a.
elephant

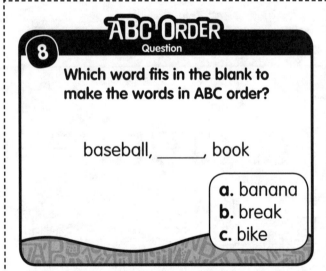

ABC Order
Question

8

Which word fits in the blank to make the words in ABC order?

baseball, _____, book

a. banana
b. break
c. bike

ABC Order
Answer

8

c. bike

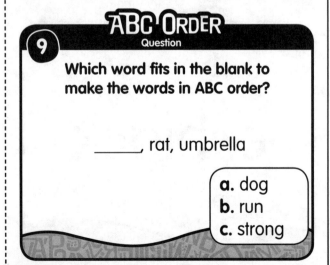

ABC Order
Question

9

Which word fits in the blank to make the words in ABC order?

_____, rat, umbrella

a. dog
b. run
c. strong

ABC Order
Answer

9

a. dog

Cooperative Learning & Grammar
Kagan Publishing • 1 (800) 933-2667 • www.KaganOnline.com

ABC ORDER
Quiz-Quiz-Trade

Instructions: Cut out each card along the dotted line. Then fold each card in half so the question is on one side and the answer is on the back. Glue or tape the cards together to keep the answers and questions on opposite sides.

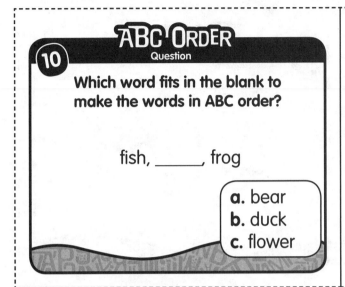

ABC ORDER
Question

10

Which word fits in the blank to make the words in ABC order?

fish, _____, frog

a. bear
b. duck
c. flower

ABC ORDER
Answer

10

c. flower

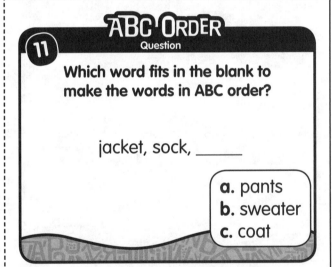

ABC ORDER
Question

11

Which word fits in the blank to make the words in ABC order?

jacket, sock, _____

a. pants
b. sweater
c. coat

ABC ORDER
Answer

11

b. sweater

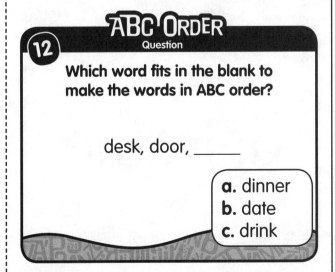

ABC ORDER
Question

12

Which word fits in the blank to make the words in ABC order?

desk, door, _____

a. dinner
b. date
c. drink

ABC ORDER
Answer

12

c. drink

Instructions: Cut out each card along the dotted line. Then fold each card in half so the question is on one side and the answer is on the back. Glue or tape the cards together to keep the answers and questions on opposite sides.

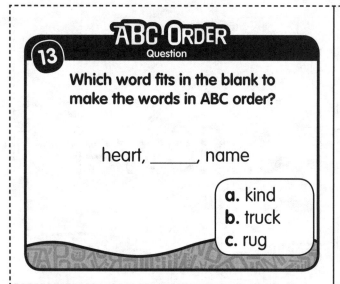

ABC ORDER
Question

13

Which word fits in the blank to make the words in ABC order?

heart, _____, name

a. kind
b. truck
c. rug

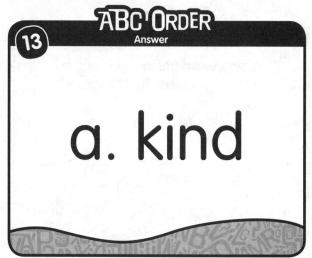

ABC ORDER
Answer

13

a. kind

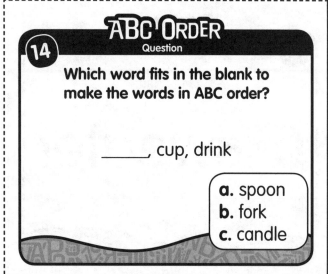

ABC ORDER
Question

14

Which word fits in the blank to make the words in ABC order?

_____, cup, drink

a. spoon
b. fork
c. candle

ABC ORDER
Answer

14

c. candle

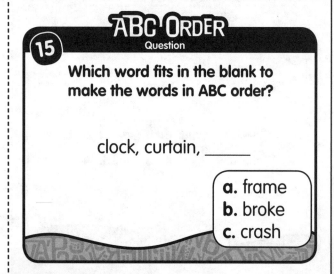

ABC ORDER
Question

15

Which word fits in the blank to make the words in ABC order?

clock, curtain, _____

a. frame
b. broke
c. crash

ABC ORDER
Answer

15

a. frame

Cooperative Learning & Grammar
Kagan Publishing • 1 (800) 933-2667 • www.KaganOnline.com

SPELLING
RallyCoach/Sage-N-Scribe

Instructions: Take turns working with your partner to choose the word that is spelled correctly. Fill in the circle with the correct answer. Use RallyCoach or Sage-N-Scribe to solve the problem.

PARTNER A

Name _____

1
- ○ money
- ○ monee
- ○ mony

2
- ○ frend
- ○ friend
- ○ freind

3
- ○ shcool
- ○ school
- ○ schol

4
- ○ very
- ○ vry
- ○ viry

5
- ○ geting
- ○ gitting
- ○ getting

6
- ○ something
- ○ sumthing
- ○ somtheng

PARTNER B

Name _____

1
- ○ aunther
- ○ another
- ○ enuther

2
- ○ either
- ○ ethir
- ○ iethar

3
- ○ becuz
- ○ beckaus
- ○ because

4
- ○ sid
- ○ sade
- ○ said

5
- ○ thought
- ○ thot
- ○ thuht

6
- ○ asced
- ○ asket
- ○ asked

SPELLING
RallyCoach/Sage-N-Scribe

Instructions: Listen to your teacher read the word aloud. Write the word on your paper. Using RallyCoach or Sage-N-Scribe, check with your partner to be sure it is correct.

PARTNER A

Name _____

1 _____

2 _____

3 _____

4 _____

5 _____

6 _____

7 _____

PARTNER B

Name _____

1 _____

2 _____

3 _____

4 _____

5 _____

6 _____

7 _____

Cooperative Learning & Grammar
Kagan Publishing • 1 (800) 933-2667 • www.KaganOnline.com

Instructions: Read the words aloud for students to write correctly on their papers. Make sure to give students enough time to discuss spelling with their partners.

100 Most Commonly Misspelled Words

1	again	21	course	41	him	61	people	81	things
2	all right	22	cousin	42	interesting	62	pretty	82	thought
3	always	23	decided	43	its	63	received	83	threw
4	an	24	didn't	44	it's	64	running	84	through
5	and	25	different	45	jumped	65	said	85	to
6	animals	26	dropped	46	knew	66	school	86	together
7	another	27	every	47	know	67	some	87	too
8	around	28	February	48	let's	68	something	88	tried
9	asked	29	first	49	like	69	sometimes	89	two
10	babies	30	for	50	little	70	started	90	until
11	beautiful	31	friend	51	looked	71	stopped	91	very
12	because	32	friends	52	many	72	surprise	92	wanted
13	before	33	frightened	53	money	73	swimming	93	went
14	believe	34	from	54	morning	74	than	94	were
15	bought	35	getting	55	mother	75	that's	95	when
16	came	36	going	56	name	76	their	96	where
17	caught	37	happening	57	named	77	then	97	with
18	children	38	hear	58	off	78	there	98	women
19	clothes	39	heard	59	once	79	they	99	would
20	coming	40	here	60	our	80	they're	100	you're

SPELLING
Find-N-Fix

Instructions: For each problem, find the misspelled word. Indicate which is incorrect using your Find-N-Fix cards. When your team agrees, spell the word correctly in the box.

1 **Which of the following is NOT spelled correctly?**

a. rat

b. sat

c. kat

Fix the Word

2 **Which of the following is NOT spelled correctly?**

a. luve

b. dove

c. gloves

Fix the Word

3 **Which of the following is NOT spelled correctly?**

a. over

b. uven

c. cover

Fix the Word

4 **Which of the following is NOT spelled correctly?**

a. last

b. pass

c. neest

Fix the Word

Cooperative Learning & Grammar
Kagan Publishing • 1 (800) 933-2667 • www.KaganOnline.com

SPELLING
Find Someone Who

Instructions: Pair up and take turns filling in the circle of the word that is spelled correctly. Don't forget to get your partner's initials.

1
- ○ think
- ○ thinke
- ○ thunke

Initials

2
- ○ doese
- ○ does
- ○ doez

Initials

3
- ○ lakee
- ○ lacke
- ○ lake

Initials

4
- ○ love
- ○ luve
- ○ luvee

Initials

5
- ○ sed
- ○ seid
- ○ said

Initials

6
- ○ liddle
- ○ litdle
- ○ little

Initials

7
- ○ was
- ○ wuz
- ○ wez

Initials

8
- ○ they
- ○ thay
- ○ tey

Initials

9
- ○ hu
- ○ who
- ○ huo

Initials

Instructions: Cut out each card along the dotted line. Then fold each card in half so the question is on one side and the answer is on the back. Glue or tape the cards together to keep the answers and questions on opposite sides.

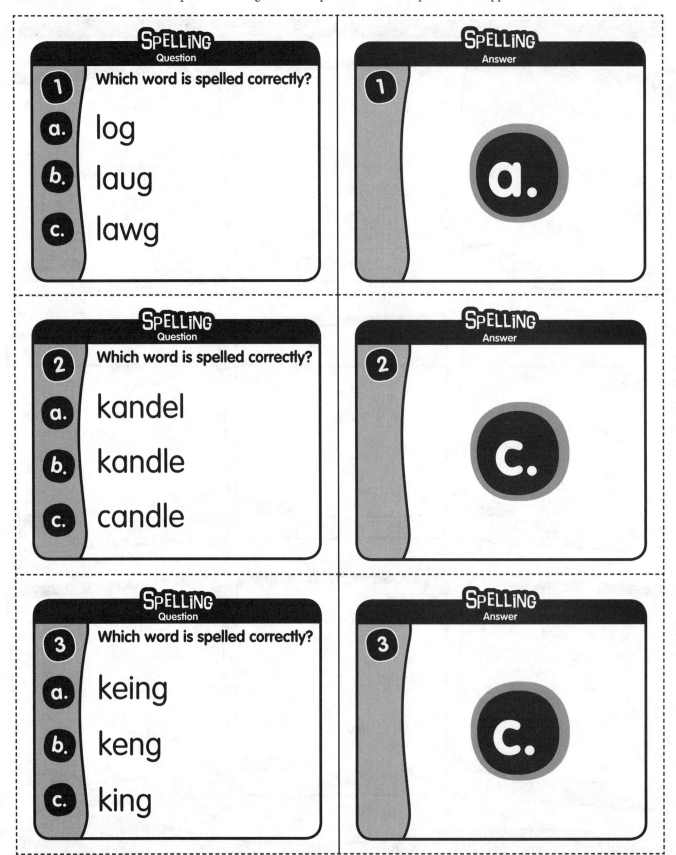

Cooperative Learning & Grammar
Kagan Publishing • 1 (800) 933-2667 • www.KaganOnline.com

Instructions: Cut out each card along the dotted line. Then fold each card in half so the question is on one side and the answer is on the back. Glue or tape the cards together to keep the answers and questions on opposite sides.

Spelling
Quiz-Quiz-Trade

Instructions: Cut out each card along the dotted line. Then fold each card in half so the question is on one side and the answer is on the back. Glue or tape the cards together to keep the answers and questions on opposite sides.

Spelling
Question

7 Which word is spelled correctly?

a. sisers

b. sciccers

c. scissors

Spelling
Answer

7

c.

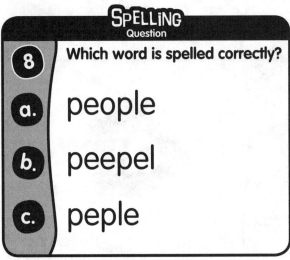

Spelling
Question

8 Which word is spelled correctly?

a. people

b. peepel

c. peple

Spelling
Answer

8

a.

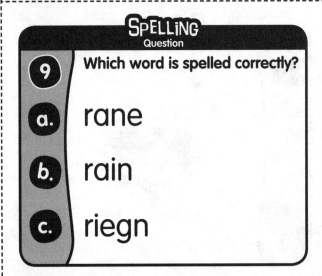

Spelling
Question

9 Which word is spelled correctly?

a. rane

b. rain

c. riegn

Spelling
Answer

9

b.

Cooperative Learning & Grammar
Kagan Publishing • 1 (800) 933-2667 • www.KaganOnline.com

Instructions: Cut out each card along the dotted line. Then fold each card in half so the question is on one side and the answer is on the back. Glue or tape the cards together to keep the answers and questions on opposite sides.

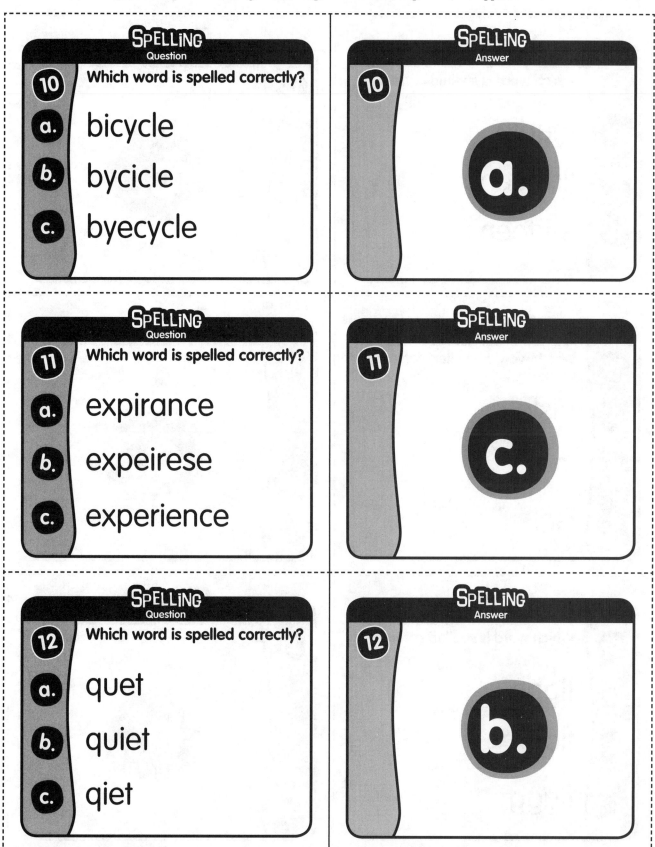

SPELLING Question

10 Which word is spelled correctly?

a. bicycle

b. bycicle

c. byecycle

SPELLING Answer

10 **a.**

SPELLING Question

11 Which word is spelled correctly?

a. expirance

b. expeirese

c. experience

SPELLING Answer

11 **c.**

SPELLING Question

12 Which word is spelled correctly?

a. quet

b. quiet

c. qiet

SPELLING Answer

12 **b.**

Instructions: Cut out each card along the dotted line. Then fold each card in half so the question is on one side and the answer is on the back. Glue or tape the cards together to keep the answers and questions on opposite sides.

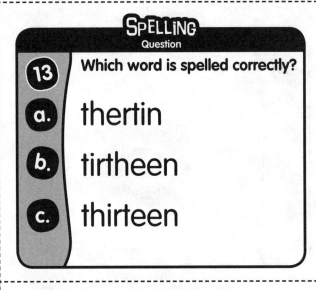

SPELLING
Question

13 Which word is spelled correctly?

a. thertin

b. tirtheen

c. thirteen

SPELLING
Answer

13

c.

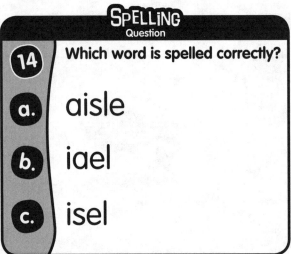

SPELLING
Question

14 Which word is spelled correctly?

a. aisle

b. iael

c. isel

SPELLING
Answer

14

a.

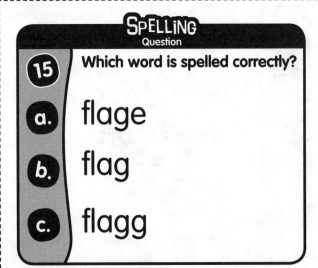

SPELLING
Question

15 Which word is spelled correctly?

a. flage

b. flag

c. flagg

SPELLING
Answer

15

b.

Cooperative Learning & Grammar
Kagan Publishing • 1 (800) 933-2667 • www.KaganOnline.com

SPELLING
Quiz-Quiz-Trade

Instructions: Cut out each card along the dotted line. Then fold each card in half so the question is on one side and the answer is on the back. Glue or tape the cards together to keep the answers and questions on opposite sides.

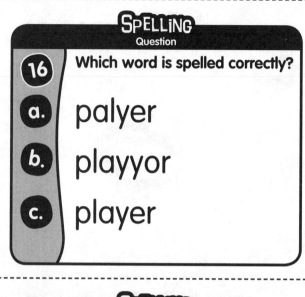

SPELLING
Question

16 Which word is spelled correctly?

a. palyer

b. playyor

c. player

SPELLING
Answer

16

c.

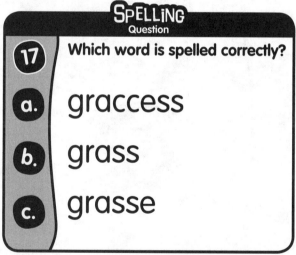

SPELLING
Question

17 Which word is spelled correctly?

a. graccess

b. grass

c. grasse

SPELLING
Answer

17

b.

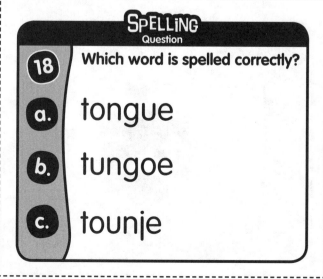

SPELLING
Question

18 Which word is spelled correctly?

a. tongue

b. tungoe

c. tounje

SPELLING
Answer

18

a.

Spelling
Quiz-Quiz-Trade

Instructions: Cut out each card along the dotted line. Then fold each card in half so the question is on one side and the answer is on the back. Glue or tape the cards together to keep the answers and questions on opposite sides.

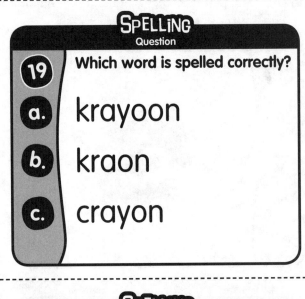

SPELLING
Question

19 Which word is spelled correctly?

a. krayoon

b. kraon

c. crayon

SPELLING
Answer

19

c.

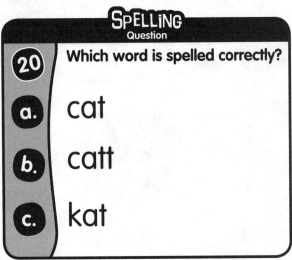

SPELLING
Question

20 Which word is spelled correctly?

a. cat

b. catt

c. kat

SPELLING
Answer

20

a.

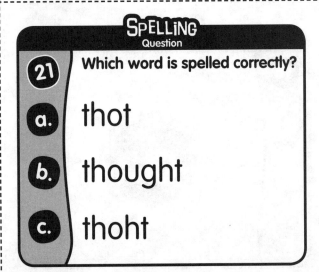

SPELLING
Question

21 Which word is spelled correctly?

a. thot

b. thought

c. thoht

SPELLING
Answer

21

b.

Cooperative Learning & Grammar
Kagan Publishing • 1 (800) 933-2667 • www.KaganOnline.com

Instructions: Cut out each card along the dotted line. Then fold each card in half so the question is on one side and the answer is on the back. Glue or tape the cards together to keep the answers and questions on opposite sides.

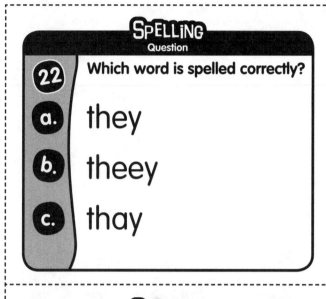

SPELLING
Question

22 Which word is spelled correctly?

a. they

b. theey

c. thay

SPELLING
Answer

22

a.

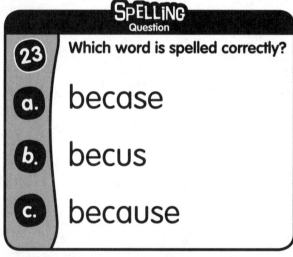

SPELLING
Question

23 Which word is spelled correctly?

a. becase

b. becus

c. because

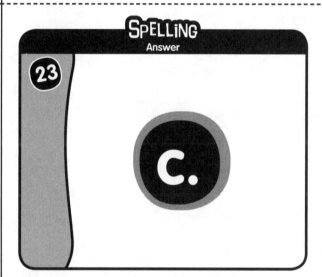

SPELLING
Answer

23

c.

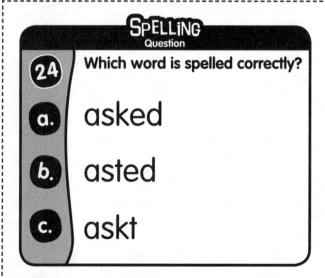

SPELLING
Question

24 Which word is spelled correctly?

a. asked

b. asted

c. askt

SPELLING
Answer

24

a.

ANSWER KEY

Answer Key

(Page 20)   Words that Are Almost Alike
RallyCoach/Sage-N-Scribe

Partner A		Partner B	
1. c. large	3. c. shout	1. c. skinny	3. b. fast
2. a. quick	4. b. sleepy	2. b. freezing	4. a. quiet

(Page 21)   Synonyms/Almost Alike
Find-N-Fix

1. c. dark–light   2. b. boy–girl   3. a. up–down   4. c. friend–enemy

(Page 22)   Words that Are Alike
Find Someone Who

1. shut	3. big	5. ill
2. shout	4. tiny	6. unhappy

(Pages 23–24)   Words that Are Alike
Fan-N-Pick/Showdown

Page 23		Page 24	
1. b. mad	4. a. tiny	7. c. father	10. b. pick
2. b. large	5. c. silent	8. a. garbage	11. a. mix
3. a. start	6. c. baby	9. c. simple	12. c. right

(Page 25)   Opposites
RallyCoach/Sage-N-Scribe

Partner A		Partner B	
1. c. young	3. c. go	1. b. thin	3. a. close
2. a. night	4. a. dry	2. c. cry	4. b. down

(Page 26)   Antonyms/Opposties
Find-N-Fix

1. c. rich–wealthy   2. b. choose–pick   3. a. tiny–small   4. b. dad–father

(Page 27)   Opposites
Find Someone Who

1. closed	3. lost	5. left
2. night	4. old	6. empty

(Pages 28–29)   Opposites
Fan-N-Pick/Showdown

Page 28		Page 29	
1. a. low	4. a. wrong	7. a. none	10. a. fast
2. b. hot	5. a. quiet	8. c. last	11. c. subtract
3. c. night	6. c. fat	9. b. forget	12. c. cold

Cooperative Learning & Grammar
Kagan Publishing • 1 (800) 933-2667 • www.KaganOnline.com

Answer Key

Cooperative Learning & Grammar
Kagan Publishing • 1 (800) 933-2667 • www.KaganOnline.com

(Page 32)

ACTION WORDS
RallyCoach/Sage-N-Scribe

PARTNER A

1. asked
2. write
3. works

PARTNER B

1. built
2. zipped
3. flies

(Pages 33–34)

ACTION WORDS
Find Someone Who

(Page 33)

1. hop
2. swim
3. eat
4. climb
5. write
6. fly

(Page 34)

1. c. kick
2. c. clap
3. a. brush
4. b. dance
5. a. yell
6. a. run
7. c. eat
8. c. talk
9. a. dive

(Pages 35–36)

ACTION WORDS
Fan-N-Pick/Showdown

Page 35

1. ran
2. ran
3. kicked
4. hopped
5. swam
6. cooked

Page 36

7. drew
8. chew
9. drove
10. climbed
11. sleeps
12. cut

(Pages 44–45)

USING ACTION WORDS
RallyCoach/Sage-N-Scribe

(Page 44)

PARTNER A

1. b. put
2. a. swimming
3. a. yelled
4. b. cried
5. c. stopped

PARTNER B

1. c. kicked
2. a. ringing
3. c. rushing
4. b. clean
5. a. pick

(Page 45)

1. Kolby _gave_ his mother a present.
   Max is _giving_ the dog a bath.
   I will _give_ you an apple for lunch.
2. Najem is _climbing_ the stairs.
   The squirrel _climbs_ to the top of the tree.
   Yesterday, I _climbed_ up steep hills.
3. Please do not _run_ in the hallway.
   Lynn _runs_ faster than a train.
   I _ran_ the mile race at the track meet.

1. I was _playing_ with my toy cars in the sand.
   Preston _played_ outside and got all muddy.
   Clint _plays_ the guitar and sings.
2. Kyle _talks_ too loudly in the library.
   Michelle _talked_ on the phone to her dad.
   Stefanie is _talking_ about her new book.
3. Shawna is _reading_ an adventure book.
   Mrs. McKoy loves to _read_ to her students.
   Brandon _reads_ in an excited voice.

(Page 46)

IS, AM, ARE
Find Someone Who

1. b. am
2. a. is
3. c. are
4. b. am
5. a. is
6. c. are
7. a. is
8. c. are
9. b. am

Answer Key

(Page 47)

ACTION WORDS
Find Someone Who

1. ran
2. swam
3. wrote
4. drove
5. drew
6. ate

(Page 48)

PAST & PRESENT ACTION WORDS
Find Someone Who

Past Tense Action Words

1. wrote
2. swam
3. ran
4. walked
5. blew
6. dove
7. jumped
8. came
9. ate

Present Tense Action Words

1. write
2. swim
3. run
4. walk
5. blow
6. dive
7. jump
8. come
9. eat

(Pages 49–50)

VERB USAGE
Fan-N-Pick/Showdown

Page 49

1. were
2. was
3. were
4. were
5. Was
6. was

Page 50

7. were
8. were
9. was
10. was
11. was
12. was

(Pages 61–62)

DESCRIBING WORDS
RallyCoach/Sage-N-Scribe

(Page 61)

PARTNER A

1. long
2. dirty
3. green

PARTNER B

1. fluffy
2. strudy
3. fresh

(Page 62)

Answers will vary.

Answers will vary.

(Pages 63–64)

DESCRIBING WORDS
Find Someone Who

(Page 63)

1. b. cold
2. c. huge
3. a. loud
4. b. hot
5. c. happy
6. a. wet
7. b. bright
8. a. round
9. b. weak

(Page 64)

1. furry
2. cold
3. hot
4. fragile
5. sharp
6. wet

(Pages 65–66)

DESCRIBING WORDS
Fan-N-Pick/Showdown

Answers will vary.

Cooperative Learning & Grammar
Kagan Publishing • 1 (800) 933-2667 • www.KaganOnline.com

Answer Key

(Pages 75)
TYPES OF NOUNS
RallyCoach/Sage-N-Scribe

PARTNER A

1. hospital
   farm
2. marble
   computer
3. parent
   singer

PARTNER B

1. garage
   park
2. train
   blanket
3. baker
   author

(Pages 76)
IDENTIFYING NOUNS
RallyCoach/Sage-N-Scribe

PARTNER A

1. c. book
2. c. balloon
3. c. castle

PARTNER B

1. c. truck
2. b. flowers
3. a. jacket

(Page 77)
NOUNS
Find Someone Who

1. thing
2. person
3. thing
4. person
5. thing
6. place
7. place
8. thing
9. person

(Pages 78–79)
NOUNS
Fan-N-Pick/Showdown

Page 78

1. The (house) had one (dog.)
2. The (cat) ran to the (girl.)
3. The (door) shut in the (wind.)
4. (Lily's) (frog) hopped away.
5. The big (computer) fell on the (floor.)
6. (Mom) made (pizza.)

Page 79

7. The (baby) crawled to the (toy.)
8. The (baseball) hit the (window.)
9. The (phone) rang in the (kitchen.)
10. (Tires) roll down the (street.)
11. The (pond) had two (fish.)
12. Can (Sally) go to the (park?)

(Page 87)
PLURAL NOUNS
RallyCoach/Sage-N-Scribe

PARTNER A

1. birds
2. shirts
3. toys
4. bushes
5. sandwiches

PARTNER B

1. trees
2. couches
3. phones
4. monkeys
5. foxes

(Page 88)
PLURAL NOUNS
Find Someone Who

1. pencils
2. cat
3. drum
4. ducks
5. boys
6. shirt

Answer Key

(Page 89)

NOUNS & ACTION WORDS REVIEW
RallyCoach/Sage-N-Scribe

PARTNER A

1. Leonard (wrote) his name on the paper.
2. The water (runs) quickly down the stream.
3. The alarm clock (chirps) loudly in the room.
4. A rainbow (stretches) across the sky.
5. The movie (plays) on the television and the computer.
6. Mom (packed) soda, sandwiches, and carrots for the picnic.

PARTNER B

1. The puppets (danced) in the show.
2. A monkey (climbed) the tree.
3. The boat (soared) through the lake and streams.
4. A hamster (spins) his wheel in the large cage.
5. The teacher (reads) a book to the students.
6. A skateboard (rolls) down the empty street.

(Page 90)

NOUNS, ACTION WORDS, & DESCRIBING WORDS REVIEW
RallyCoach/Sage-N-Scribe

PARTNER A

1. Larry (kicked) the red ball.
2. The dirty shirt needs to be (washed.)
3. The old dinosaur (growled) loudly.
4. Michele (planted) yellow and pink flowers in her garden.
5. The noisy crowd (cheered) loudly for the winning team.
6. Millie (swam) in the refreshing lake.
7. The train (sped) down the long tracks.
8. The baby (cries) for a warm bottle.
9. James (walked) the black dog.
10. The green grass (grows) in the light.

PARTNER B

1. The warm pancakes (filled) my belly.
2. My red shoes (fit) my feet like a sock.
3. The purple balloon (floated) in the sky.
4. Dee (baked) fresh rolls and yummy cupcakes.
5. The grand piano (made) beautiful music from the stage.
6. Brett (reads) on the comfy sofa.
7. The curious monkey (climbed) a tree.
8. Fredrick (told) me a silly story.
9. The loud thunder (shook) the house.
10. The large clock (chimed) in the kitchen.

(Page 91)

NOUNS, DESCRIBING WORDS, & ACTION WORDS REVIEW
Find Someone Who

Noun		Describing Word		Action Word	
teacher	boy	pretty	ugly	jump	chew
girl	computer	old	fat	run	swim
man		big		kick	

(Page 92)

NOUNS & ACTION WORDS
Find Someone Who

1. frog *(noun)*
   jump *(action)*
2. dog *(noun)*
   catch *(action)*
3. girl *(noun)*
   eat *(action)*
4. boy *(noun)*
   draw *(action)*
5. cat *(noun)*
   sleep *(action)*
6. man *(noun)*
   drive *(action)*

Cooperative Learning & Grammar
Kagan Publishing • 1 (800) 933-2667 • www.KaganOnline.com

Answer Key

(Page 93)

PRONOUNS

RallyCoach/Sage-N-Scribe

PARTNER A		PARTNER B	
1. He	4. It	1. It	4. She
2. it	5. them	2. It	5. it
3. We		3. They	

(Pages 94–95)

PRONOUNS

(Page 94)

Find Someone Who

1. a. she	3. c. he	5. b. them
2. c. they	4. c. he	6. a. I

(Page 95)

1. How long will (she) be gone?
2. (He) forgot the homework.
3. Did (they) enjoy the movie?
4. When will (we) get to the park?
5. John lost (his) mittens.
6. Did (her) mom pick up the pizza?
7. (He) ran down the street.
8. How long did (it) take them?
9. Did Shelly talk to (him) yesterday?

(Pages 96–97)

PRONOUNS

Fan-N-Pick/Showdown

Page 96		**Page 97**	
1. b. He	4. b. him	7. c. They	10. b. It
2. a. She	5. a. We	8. c. them	11. a. we
3. a. It	6. c. They	9. b. his	12. a. he

(Page 98)

A OR AN?

RallyCoach/Sage-N-Scribe

PARTNER A		PARTNER B	
1. a	5. a	1. An	5. an
2. a	6. an	2. a	6. a
3. an	7. a	3. a	7. a
4. an		4. an	

(Page 99)

ARTICLES

Find Someone Who

1. an	4. an	7. an
2. a	5. a	8. a
3. a	6. a	9. a

(Pages 100–101)

ARTICLES

Fan-N-Pick/Showdown

Page 100		**Page 101**	
1. a	4. a	7. a	10. an
2. an	5. an	8. an	11. a
3. a	6. an	9. a	12. a

Answer Key

(Page 102) COMPOUND WORDS
RallyCoach/Sage-N-Scribe

PARTNER A

1.	sand	4.	walk
2.	cake	5.	bow
3.	hot		

PARTNER B

1.	sail	4.	pan
2.	corn	5.	boy
3.	foot		

(Page 103) COMPOUND WORDS
Find Someone Who

1.	b.	box	6.	a.	light
2.	c.	shine	7.	c.	knob
3.	b.	ball	8.	a.	brush
4.	a.	thing	9.	c.	day
5.	b.	bow			

(Page 110) WRITING CONTRACTIONS
RallyCoach/Sage-N-Scribe

PARTNER A

1.	don't	4.	it's
2.	I'm	5.	he's
3.	they're		

PARTNER B

1.	I'll	4.	she's
2.	haven't	5.	he'll
3.	we're		

(Page 111) CONTRACTIONS
RallyCoach/Sage-N-Scribe

PARTNER A

1.	don't	5.	she'll
2.	doesn't	6.	don't
3.	won't	7.	didn't
4.	can't	8.	won't

PARTNER B

1.	won't	5.	We're
2.	isn't	6.	isn't
3.	I'm	7.	doesn't
4.	haven't	8.	can't

(Page 112) CONTRACTIONS
Find Someone Who

1.	a.	don't	4.	b.	shouldn't	7.	b.	she'll
2.	c.	I'd	5.	a.	can't	8.	c.	he'd
3.	c.	couldn't	6.	c.	that's	9.	a.	you're

(Pages 113–114) CONTRACTIONS
Fan-N-Pick/Showdown

Page 113

1.	c.	I've
2.	a.	doesn't
3.	b.	didn't
4.	b.	can't
5.	c.	I'm
6.	b.	She'll

Page 114

1.	b.	haven't
2.	b.	wasn't
3.	a.	they're
4.	c.	He's
5.	b.	they'll
6.	c.	isn't

Cooperative Learning & Grammar
Kagan Publishing • 1 (800) 933-2667 • www.KaganOnline.com

Answer Key

(Page 128)
CAPITALIZATION AT THE BEGINNING OF THE SENTENCE
RallyCoach/Sage-N-Scribe

PARTNER A

1. *It*
   ~~it~~ is time to go home.
2. *My*
   ~~my~~ dog is named Fido.
3. *When*
   ~~when~~ can I dance?
4. *Do*
   ~~do~~ not forget a coat.

PARTNER B

1. *My*
   ~~my~~ teddy bear is black.
2. *The*
   ~~the~~ picture is very pretty.
3. *His*
   ~~his~~ sister is crying.
4. *The*
   ~~the~~ dancer is stunning.

(Pages 129)
CAPITAL LETTERS—DAYS OF THE WEEK
Find Someone Who

1. Thursday
2. Tuesday
3. Saturday
4. Monday
5. Friday
6. Wednesday

(Pages 130–131)
CAPITAL LETTERS
Fan-N-Pick/Showdown

Page 130

1. *Officer John*
   ~~officer john~~ visited our classroom.
2. *Saturday*
   ~~saturday~~
3. We live on planet ~~earth~~. *Earth*
4. *New York*
   ~~new york~~
5. *Pizza Hut®*
   ~~pizza hut~~
6. *I* ~~i~~ went to ~~burger king®~~ for lunch. *Burger King®*

Page 131

7. *I* ~~i~~ was born in ~~october~~. *October*
8. *I* ~~i~~ live on ~~bird lane~~. *Bird Lane*
9. *Chicago, Illinois*
   ~~chicago, illinois~~
10. *We* ~~we~~ went to ~~stockstill park~~ for a field trip. *Stockstill Park*
11. *Mary* ~~mary~~ read ~~goodnight moon~~. *Goodnight Moon*
12. *Valentine's Day*
    ~~valentine's day~~

(Page 140)
COMMAS IN A LIST
RallyCoach/Sage-N-Scribe

PARTNER A

1. Megan brought cookies, cake, and soda to the party.
2. Karen bought a teddy bear, doll, and a purse at the store.
3. Kolby picked up his movies, put away his clothes, and made his bed.
4. My favorite books are about animals, people, and faraway places.
5. My dad made tacos, burritos, and salad for dinner.
6. I packed my towel, swimsuit, bucket, and umbrella for my beach party.

PARTNER B

1. Caleb's favorite foods are ice cream, pizza, and carrots.
2. My bedroom has a new bed, bookshelf, and rug.
3. I have math, spelling, and reading homework to do tonight.
4. The doctor checked my toes, legs, and knees after my fall.
5. We got the new kitten a pillow, food, and a water bowl.
6. Jessica took her pajamas, blanket, and slippers to the sleepover.

Answer Key

(Page 141) COMMAS IN DATES & PLACES
RallyCoach/Sage-N-Scribe

PARTNER A

1. March 10, 1978
2. Murfessburo, Arkansas
3. Sunday, December 27, 2011
4. Lake Tahoe, California

PARTNER B

1. Mason, Ohio
2. Monday, February 1, 1958
3. Colorado Springs, Colorado
4. June 23, 2007

(Page 142) COMMAS
Find Someone Who

1. a. January, 4 1980
2. b. I live in Branson, MO.
3. c. Joe brought books, paper, and pencils.
4. c. We took our vacation in Springfield, Illinois.
5. c. Dear Grandma,
6. c. Your daughter,

(Page 143) WRITING DATES
Find Someone Who

1. ~~januray~~ January 6, 2011
2. ~~march~~ March 2, 1990
3. ~~april~~ April 8, 1970
4. b. December 6, 1980
5. ~~october~~ October 10, 2010
6. c. August 3, 1997
7. ~~july~~ July 17, 2009
8. a. May 5, 2009
9. ~~november~~ November 25, 2012

(Pages 144–145) COMMAS
Fan-N-Pick/Showdown

Page 144

1. I live in Austin, Texas.
2. I was born on January 12, 2004.
3. Yours truly,
4. I like to read, write, and play games.
5. My dog can catch sticks, balls, and newspapers.
6. Dear Grandma,

Page 145

7. We will be going to St. Louis, Missouri for vacation.
8. Maria brought cupcakes, plates, and cups to the party.
9. Please bring yarn, glue, and crayons to the carpet.
10. The last day of school is May 22, 2013.
11. Your Daughter,
12. Dear Mr. President,

(Page 146) ENDING PUNCTUATION
RallyCoach/Sage-N-Scribe

PARTNER A

1. .
2. !
3. ?
4. .
5. .
6. !

PARTNER B

1. .
2. ?
3. .
4. !
5. .
6. !

Cooperative Learning & Grammar
Kagan Publishing • 1 (800) 933-2667 • www.KaganOnline.com

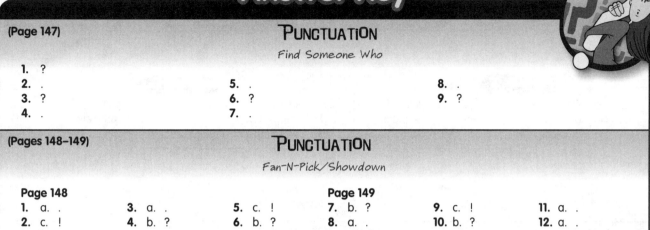

Answer Key

PUNCTUATION

Find Someone Who

(Page 147)

1. ?
2. .
3. ?
4. .

5. .
6. ?
7. .

8. .
9. ?

(Pages 148–149)

PUNCTUATION

Fan-N-Pick/Showdown

Page 148

1. a. .
2. c. !

3. a. .
4. b. ?

5. c. !
6. b. ?

Page 149

7. b. ?
8. a. .

9. c. !
10. b. ?

11. a. .
12. a. .

Answer Key

(Pages 152–153)
COMPLETE SENTENCES
RallyCoach/Sage-N-Scribe

(Page 152)

PARTNER A

1. Complete	4. Complete
2. Not Complete	5. Not Complete
3. Not Complete	

PARTNER B

1. Not Complete	4. Complete
2. Complete	5. Not Complete
3. Not Complete	

(Page 153)

1. ball	3. phone
2. leaf	4. book

1. car	3. house
2. rabbit	4. boy

(Page 154)
COMPLETE SENTENCES
Find-N-Fix

Answers may very.
1. b. Kolby kick.
2. a. Down the street.
3. c. In December.
4. a. Up in the air.

(Page 155)
COMPLETE SENTENCES
Find Someone Who

1. Yes
2. Yes
3. No
4. No
5. Yes
6. Yes
7. Yes
8. No
9. Yes

(Pages 156–157)
COMPLETE SENTENCES
Fan-N-Pick/Showdown

Answers will vary.

(Page 166)
SENTENCE WORD ORDER
RallyCoach/Sage-N-Scribe

PARTNER A

1. The tree is growing really tall.
   ~~growing tree tall. really The is~~
2. My dog is wanting to play fetch.
   ~~fetch. dog is play wanting My to~~
3. It is time to go to school.
   ~~go is school. time It to~~
4. The pig is rolling in the mud.
   ~~pig the in The mud. is rolling~~

PARTNER B

1. Can you read this book to me again?
   ~~you again? read Can book this me to~~
2. The play will begin in one hour.
   ~~begin play The hour. will one in~~
3. The baby wants his blanket.
   ~~blanket. wants baby The his~~
4. It is time to eat lunch.
   ~~is lunch. to eat It time~~

(Page 167)
SENTENCE WORD ORDER
Find Someone Who

1. The dog is hiding under the bed.
   ~~bed. hiding The under os the dog.~~
2. Sloan wants a doll for her birthday.
   ~~birthday. wants for a her Sloan doll~~
3. The rabbit hops down the street.
   ~~down rabbit The street. hops the~~
4. Billy lost his teddy bear in the park.
   ~~lost park. his the teddy bear Billy at~~
5. Mrs. Glenn read us a book.
   ~~Mrs. book. us read Glenn~~
6. I got a letter in the mail.
   ~~I mail. a in got the letter~~

Cooperative Learning & Grammar
Kagan Publishing • 1 (800) 933-2667 • www.KaganOnline.com

Answer Key

SENTENCE WORD ORDER
Fan-N-Pick/Showdown

Page 168

1. The computer broke today.
   ~~broke computer today The.~~
2. The dog jumped a fence.
   ~~dog a fence jumped The.~~
3. The rug had a stain.
   ~~stain had rug The a.~~
4. Can we watch a movie?
   ~~movie a watch Can we?~~
5. My mom drives a blue car.
   ~~mom My drives a car blue.~~
6. The cow ate the grass.
   ~~grass The ate the cow.~~

Page 169

1. When does Johnny come home?
   ~~Johnny come When home does?~~
2. Kolby enjoys hamburger pizza.
   ~~enjoys pizza hamburger Kolby.~~
3. Lucy won the race.
   ~~won race Lucy the.~~
4. The pond was frozen.
   ~~pond The frozen was.~~
5. Mario likes video games.
   ~~games Mario video likes.~~
6. Ducks fly south for the winter.
   ~~fly Ducks south winter for the.~~

TYPES OF SENTENCES: STATEMENTS
RallyCoach/Sage-N-Scribe

PARTNER A

1. Statement
2. Not a Statement
3. Not a Statement
4. Statement
5. Statement

PARTNER B

1. Not a Statement
2. Statement
3. Statement
4. Not a Statement
5. Not a Statement

(Page 171)

1. It is really raining outside.
2. I love to eat apples for lunch.
3. We are going to swim at the pool.

1. Grandaddly is coming to visit.
2. The car needs more gas.
3. The balloons are popping.

TYPES OF SENTENCES: QUESTIONS
RallyCoach/Sage-N-Scribe

PARTNER A

1. Question
2. Not Question
3. Question
4. Not Question
5. Question

PARTNER B

1. Question
2. Question
3. Not Question
4. Not Question
5. Question

(Page 173)

1. Where are my shoes ?
2. What is for lunch ?
3. Why are the pigs in the mud ?

1. Can I have pizza for dinner ?
2. How do I zip my coat ?
3. Did you read this book ?

TYPES OF SENTENCES: EXCLAMATIONS
RallyCoach/Sage-N-Scribe

PARTNER A

1. Not Exclamation
2. Exclamation
3. Exclamation
4. Exclamation
5. Not Exclamation

PARTNER B

1. Not Exclamation
2. Not Exclamation
3. Exclamation
4. Exclamation
5. Exclamation

Answer Key

(Pages 174–175) *(continued)*
(Page 175)

TYPES OF SENTENCES: EXCLAMATIONS
RallyCoach/Sage-N-Scribe

PARTNER A

1. I am laughing too hard!
2. Help!
3. We won the race!

PARTNER B

1. I can't wait to see my grandma!
2. That ride was fast!
3. I see a frog!

(Pages 176–177)
(Page 176)

TYPES OF SENTENCES: COMMANDS
RallyCoach/Sage-N-Scribe

PARTNER A

1. Command
2. Not Command
3. Command
4. Not Command
5. Not Command

PARTNER B

1. Command
2. Command
3. Not Command
4. Command
5. Not Command

(Page 177)

1. Clean your room.
2. Do not touch the stove!
3. Turn off the computer.

1. Please dust the shelves.
2. Put on your coat.
3. Watch your step!

(Page 178)

TYPES OF SENTENCES: ASKING OR TELLING
RallyCoach/Sage-N-Scribe

PARTNER A

1. Telling
2. Telling
3. Asking
4. Asking
5. Telling

PARTNER B

1. Asking
2. Telling
3. Asking
4. Asking
5. Telling

(Page 179)

QUESTION, COMMAND, OR STATEMENT
Find Someone Who

1. Command
2. Question
3. Command
4. Question
5. Statement
6. Statement
7. Command
8. Question
9. Statement

(Page 180)

ASKING OR TELLING SENTENCES
Find Someone Who

1. Telling
2. Asking
3. Telling
4. Telling
5. Asking
6. Asking
7. Telling
8. Asking
9. Asking

Cooperative Learning & Grammar
Kagan Publishing • 1 (800) 933-2667 • www.KaganOnline.com

Answer Key

(Pages 181–182) SENTENCE TYPES
Fan-N-Pick/Showdown

Page 181

1. Lucy lost per pink ring⊙ *Statement*
2. The campfire was hot⊙ *Statement*
3. Will you be at the party⟨?⟩ *Question*
4. Today's fire alarm was noisy⊙ *Statement*
5. Five birds sat on a branch⊙ *Statement*
6. Get out your pencils⊙ *Command*

Page 182

1. Did you find your coat⟨?⟩ *Question*
2. Turn to page 45 in your math book⊙ *Command*
3. Do your homework before dinner⊙ *Command*
4. What is your last name⟨?⟩ *Question*
5. The shirt was too big⊙ *Statement*
6. Soccer is my favorite sport⊙ *Statement*

(Page 183) SENTENCE PARTS
RallyCoach/Sage-N-Scribe

PARTNER A

1. Our class took a field trip to the zoo.
2. The elephants moved slowly.
3. The popcorn was good to eat.
4. The bus driver drove us back to school.
5. My mom bought me an ice cream.
6. Some teachers petted the giraffe.

PARTNER B

1. The kids fed the goats at the petting zoo.
2. Big trees grew in the lion den.
3. A man was feeding the tigers.
4. A big wind blew the leaves.
5. Rain fell from the sky.
6. Everyone ran to the bus.

(Page 184) NAMING PART
Find Someone Who

1. Josh ran down the street.
2. Gabe and Beth had a picnic.
3. They fed bread to the ducks.
4. The basket tipped over in the wind.
5. The round apple was juicy.
6. The playground was crowded.
7. John took pictures of the lake.
8. The blanket got dirty.
9. The ducks ate the bread.

(Page 185) WRITING THE ACTION PART
RallyCoach/Sage-N-Scribe

PARTNER A

1. The teacher *blew the whistle.*
2. The crayons *broke into pieces.*
3. The books *sat on the shelf.*
4. The lunchroom *smelled like food.*

PARTNER B

1. Our class pet *swam in the bowl.*
2. The bell *rang three times.*
3. Juice *spilled on the floor.*
4. The kid *played at recess.*

Answer Key

(Pages 186–188)

ACTION PART
Fan-N-Pick/Showdown

Page 186
1. a. rescued the little girl.
2. c. climbed a tree.
3. b. helped the sick boy.
4. a. swam in circles.
5. c. grew tall.
6. b. drew a picture.

Page 187
7. c. delivered the package.
8. b. flew into the tree.
9. a. ate a fly.
10. a. was painted blue.
11. c. ran into the woods.
12. b. was chopped down.

Page 188
13. b. cried all night.
14. b. ran up a tree.
15. c. blew the napkin away.
16. c. bounced down the street.
17. a. went blank.
18. a. were loud.

(Pages 189–190)

NAMING & ACTION PARTS OF A SENTENCE
Fan-N-Pick/Showdown

Page 189
1. c. The baker
2. b. cooked dinner.
3. b. A strong wind
4. c. got lost.
5. a. The dog
6. a. had two pillows.

Page 190
7. a. Each sentence
8. b. The artist
9. c. Socks
10. c. The dresser
11. a. The door
12. c. Birds

Cooperative Learning & Grammar
Kagan Publishing • 1 (800) 933-2667 • www.KaganOnline.com

Answer Key

(Page 192)

ABC ORDER
RallyCoach/Sage-N-Scribe

PARTNER A

1. Necklace   Ring
2. Apple   Cake
3. Hat   Shoe

PARTNER B

1. Car   Truck
2. Drum   Guitar
3. Eye   Tooth

(Page 193)

ABC ORDER
Find-N-Fix

1. b.   ~~bike, bump, broom~~
   bike, broom, bump
2. b.   ~~boy, mom, dad~~
   boy, dad, mom

3. c.   ~~desk, door, damp~~
   damp, desk, door
4. a.   ~~said, say, sail~~
   said, sail, say

(Pages 194–195)

ABC ORDER
Find Someone Who

(Page 194)

1. E
2. P
3. u
4. m
5. H
6. j
7. d, i
8. Q, T
9. W

(Page 195)

1. Bread
2. Book
3. Apple
4. Chair
5. Boots
6. Brush
7. Glossary
8. Alaska
9. Church

(Pages 196–198)

WRITING ABC ORDER
Fan-N-Pick/Showdown

Page 196
1. all, must, say
2. boy, kite, sand
3. black, into, ride
4. eat, four, pretty
5. be, have, new
6. am, have, ran

Page 197
7. cat, me, red, two
8. are, did, out, there
9. blue, fun, it, one
10. our, she, who, with
11. and, come, go, play
12. can, like, no, the

Page 198
13. am, came, going, here
14. has, my, said, will
15. as, good, went, your
16. green, off, three, we
17. big, brown, stop, top
18. black, sit, six, white

(Pages 199–201)

ABC ORDER
Fan-N-Pick/Showdown

Page 199
1. c. bed, desk, table
2. c. dad, dog, mom
3. b. banana, peach, pear
4. b. moon, sky, star
5. b. finger, nail, ring
6. a. airplane, bike, truck

Page 200
7. a. cat, dog, mouse
8. a. door, floor, rug
9. c. Friday, Monday, Wednesday
10. c. blue, purple, yellow
11. a. ball, bat, glove
12. c. jump, play, run

Page 201
13. c. kind, pretty, smart
14. a. cup, glass, plate
15. c. basket, broom, brush
16. c. bath, soap, water
17. a. baby, boy, girl
18. b. bucket, sand, towel

Answer Key

Spe

(Page 207)

SPELLING
RallyCoach/Sage-N-Scribe

PARTNER A	PARTNER B
1. money	1. another
2. friend	2. either
3. school	3. because
4. very	4. said
5. getting	5. thought
6. something	6. asked

(Page 208)

SPELLING
RallyCoach/Sage-N-Scribe

Answers will vary.

(Page 210)

SPELLING
Find-N-Fix

1. c. ~~kat~~ *cat*
2. a. ~~luve~~ *love*
3. b. ~~uven~~ *oven*
4. c. ~~neest~~ *nest*

(Page 211)

SPELLING
Find Someone Who

1. think	4. love	7. was
2. does	5. said	8. they
3. lake	6. little	9. who

Cooperative Learning & Grammar
Kagan Publishing • 1 (800) 933-2667 • www.KaganOnline.com